WITHOUT
A HOME

Inspiring and *heartfelt* tales of small animal adoptions

ELAINE MARLIER

ILLUSTRATIONS BY JUDITH ANGELL MEYER

First Edition
January 2009

ISBN: 0-9800867-2-8

**Published in the United States
of America by:**

DNJ Books
P.O. Box 620096
Littleton, Colorado 80162
Email: info@dnjbooks.com
Website: www.dnjbooks.com

Designer

Michele Renée Ledoux
www.mledoux.com

Editor

Julia Wade Fliss
Art as Endless Possibility :: Creative Consulting
jfliss@artasendlesspossibility.com

foreword

While there is nothing wrong with buying a small companion animal—there is everything right with adopting one! The belief that small animals in shelters or rescue facilities are just unwanted animals and "never did have a home" is simply not true. Every small animal in every shelter across America has a story to tell. Whether they came from a nice, loving home, were abused by their prior owners, were neglected by their "human parents" or were abandoned somewhere, they have a history. They were not born in the shelter.

Shelters who offer these furry little critters for adoption are like a used parking lot of small animals. You can find almost any type of small animal imaginable—from mice and rats to chinchillas and ferrets to guinea pigs and rabbits. Whatever your preference, there will undoubtedly be a "furry little creature" to fit your bill. Unlike purchasing a used car that will hopefully give you years of dependable travel along the highways, adopting a small animal from a shelter or rescue center will net you a lifetime of adoring eyes, great companionship, laughter filled with "nibbley" kisses and, the greatest pleasure of all—the capture of your heart.

As a connection between two souls, the benefits of adoption are twofold. For the animal the benefit is profound. Simply stated—they know. They know you are the one who took them from the shelter or rescue center and gave them a home. They know you are the one who gave them that second chance. Although they cannot speak the words, they show their appreciation through the love and devotion they give you everyday. For the human, the benefit is profound as well. There is a certain emotional satisfaction that comes from having a loving companion who exists solely due to the gracious, unselfish, wonderful deed a human has done by adopting. It is this inside joy of the heart that comes from giving an animal the opportunity for a new life.

That is the human-animal bond.

inspirational poems

The following two poems reveal the hidden thoughts and feelings of animals who have experienced the pain of being *without a home*. Their words are heartfelt and evocative and for that reason I'm sure you'll find them as inspiring as I have.

Rescue Me

Rescue Me…

Rescue me not only with your hands, but with your heart.
I will respond to you.

Rescue me not out of pity, but out of love.
I will love you back.

Rescue me not with your self-righteousness, but with your compassion.
I will learn what you teach.

Rescue me not because of my past, but because of my future.
I will relax and enjoy.

Rescue me not simply to save, but to give me a new life.
I will appreciate your gift.

Rescue me not only with a firm hand, but with tolerance and patience.
I will please you.

Rescue me not only because of who I am, but who I am to become.
I will grow and mature.

Rescue me to not revere yourself to others, but because you want me.
I will never let you down.

Rescue me not with a hidden agenda, but with a desire to teach me.
I will be loyal and true.

Rescue me not to be chained or to fight, but to be your companion.
I will stand by your side.

Rescue me not to replace one you have lost, but to sooth your spirit.
I will cherish you.

Rescue me not to be your pet, but to be YOUR friend.
I will give you unconditional love always and forever…

Author Unknown

The Meaning of Rescue

Now that I'm home, bathed, settled and fed,
All nicely tucked into my warm new bed,
I'd like to open my baggage,
Lest I forget.
There is so much to carry–
So much to regret.

Yes, there it is, right on the top,
Let's unpack loneliness, heartache and loss.
And there by my bed hides fear and shame.
As I look on these things I tried so hard to leave,
I still have to unpack my baggage called pain.

I loved them, the others, the ones who left me,
But I wasn't good enough–for they did not want me.
Will you add to my baggage?
Or help me unpack?
Or will you just look at my things,
And take me right back?

Do you have the time to help me unpack?
To put away my baggage,
And never repack?
I pray that you do–I'm so tired you see
But I do come with baggage
Do you still want me?

Author Unknown

Table of Contents

Foreword   iii
Inspirational Poems   v

Chapter One
harry the hamster   13
    The Squeaky Wheel   15
    One Man's Trash...   33

Chapter Two
cindy the chinchilla   41
    The Importance of Love   43
    Beauty Isn't Only Skin Deep   59

Chapter Three
reggie the rat   69
    Looking for Billy   71
    The Importance of Adoption   87

Chapter Four
bonnie the bunny   95
    The Easter Present   97
    An Easter Present Times Two   113

Chapter Five
frankie the ferret   121
    Left Behind   123
    Learning How to Live   137

Martha's Words   143
A Call to Action   145

Resources   **147**

harry the hamster   **13**

cindy the chinchilla   **41**

reggie the rat   **69**

bonnie the bunny   **95**

frankie the ferret   **121**

Author

Elaine Marlier
www.dnjbooks.com

Illustrator

Judith Angell Meyer
www.fortmeyereditions.com

Designer

Michele Renée Ledoux
www.mledoux.com

Editor

Julia Wade Fliss
www.artasendlesspossibility.com

harry the hamster

CHAPTER ONE

cue shelter and takes one of us home to live with them instead of buying a new one.

A new one? That makes it sound as if I'm used. Hey…wait a minute…what are you saying? Are you saying I'm not going back home…that I won't see little Ryan anymore?

Butterball hung his head. *No, Harry you won't. I'm sorry, but you won't be seeing Ryan anymore.*

Saying nothing, Harry hobbled over to the couch and curled up on top of it. Butterball followed just seconds behind him.

It's going to be okay, Harry, really it is. You'll see. This place adopts out a lot of us all the time. You won't have to stay here long. You'll find a new family to live with real soon.

But I don't want a new family! I want to go back to my home with Maggie, Bill and little Ryan. Why can't I just go back home? I don't want to be here!

Butterball could do nothing but sigh. He had seen this depression before. Given his wisdom, one would think his stay at the Critter Heaven Small Animal Rescue had been a long one, but in actuality, he had only been there for a little over three weeks.

It'll be okay little guy…I promise it will. Just give it some time.

Harry curled up his lip. Staring at Butterball, he was consumed with disbelief. He slowly closed his eyes and drifted off to sleep. With deep, loving visions of little Ryan taking charge of his dreams, he never heard the conversation happening only two feet away.

Lulu, one of the striped Dwarf hamsters in the next cage, rested her feet on the bars, allowing her body to maintain a standing-up position.

*Hey, Butterball…*she whispered, *who's the new guy?*

Butterball watched Harry momentarily, ensuring he was completely asleep before walking to the back of the cage to face Lulu.

That's Harry. He's going to be a tough one to convince. I can already see it.

Oh, just give him a few days. When he sees all the traffic coming in and out of here and when he sees how many of us find new homes, he'll change his perspective for sure.

I don't know Lulu. I see a deeper sadness in him. He may have been one of those who had a family who truly loved him. You know, the kind that took him out of the cage a lot, played with him and let him run around the house. I don't think he was one of us.

Lulabell and Butterball did share a unique bond. They were both victims of the "little cute syndrome." They were two-of-a-kind. Both of them had been purchased for the same reason—because they looked so cute and adorable. Everyone in their new households took the responsibility of their care and welfare very seriously. They properly cleaned their cages and ensured they had fresh water and food everyday, but no one realized how much interaction with humans they really needed. The first few weeks had been great—running around the house in a ball, being played with by human hands—but all that faded quickly after the initial welcome period. It wasn't long before the two of them became objects in a cage sitting on top of a dresser. There was the occasional conversation while their cages were being cleaned and the occasional pat on the head when food was placed in their bowls, but the days of running up and down someone's shoulder had become a distant memory. Before coming to Critter Heaven Small Animal Rescue, Butterball had not been able to remember the last time he curled up in the crevasse of an arm to sleep while others watched television. He, just like Lulu, was almost grateful when he was given to the shelter. Here, the interaction with humans was almost constant and the boredom was gone. There were new adventures every day, and even more importantly, the two of them now had friends. No longer caught in a cycle of wondering what they had done to upset their owners, now all that Butterball and Lulu had to do was hope and pray that new loving arms would once again find them.

Harry stirred in his sleep. Butterball quickly looked in his direction. He could see one of his eyes open.

I'll talk with you later, Lulu. Harry's waking up.

When both of Harry's eyes completely opened, Butterball was sitting right by the couch. Harry stretched out his little front feet.

Hey there, little buddy…you okay?

Harry nodded. *Yeah, I'm okay. Who were you talking to over there?*

Butterball glanced in Lulu's direction and smiled before turning his attention back to Harry.

That's Lulu. She's a Dwarf, but she's a real sweetheart. You'll like her as soon as you get to know her.

Butterball curled up on the bedding just below the couch.

So, Harry…tell me about your life. Tell me about the family you had.

At first Harry's face revealed disappointment, but as soon as thoughts of little Ryan entered his mind, a smile quickly appeared on his face.

My family was great! I wish you could have met little Ryan. He was such a character! Every day when he would come home from school, the first thing he would do was run over to my cage and let me out. He would chase me all over the bedroom. We constantly played hide and seek, but he always found me—of course, not really always. There were lots of times I had to come out just a little bit from where I was hiding in order for him to find me!

Wow! Sounds like he really loved you.

Oh I have no doubt he did. I was always a top priority in his life. Sure he had friends that came over after school, but he never once went out to see them before he wrestled around the room with me! He was such a great kid! And he loved boasting to his friends about me. I can remember him flying in the door to his bedroom after he had been out playing with his friends, just dying to show me off. Sometimes there were three or four of them in the room at one time. I'd run under the bed, and through the giggles I could see all these feet running around trying to find me.

As soon as one head appeared under the bed, I would immediately run under the dresser. The middle of each side of it stood almost an inch and a half up off the floor. That was my favorite spot. No one could ever find me. If they looked through that space, I would simply crawl to the corner where the leg sat on the floor. Then I would always hear one of the boys scream out that I wasn't under there! Ha, it was so much fun. I fooled them all the time.

Didn't that ever worry Ryan?

Oh no. If I could tell they were getting disappointed in not finding me, or that Ryan was getting scared, I would simply stick my foot out from under the dresser, or I would run out and purposely dart right in front of them. I always had to make it look like they found me, not that I was coming out from hiding!

A hamster laugh is the funniest thing anyone could ever hear, although most humans never hear it. Butterball's laughter echoed throughout the room. It caught everyone's attention. Every hamster, in every cage, walked over to the edge of their bars to hear the story. Harry, so engrossed in his memories, never once noticed his audience.

Gosh Harry, with such a wonderful life, I can't imagine how you ended up here!

Harry stared at him, feeling the words of his statement hit him hard. He too could not believe, with the great life he had, why he would have been given away. His eyes narrowed. He thought long and hard.

I'm not really sure either. I can tell you though—it couldn't have had anything to do with Ryan. We played together all the time! I know that little boy loved me. I know all of his friends loved me too! I have no doubt!

Ester, one of the Black European hamsters, was the first stranger to speak to Harry.

Do you think it was his mother or father that made the decision?

Harry looked in Ester's direction. *What do you mean?*

Well, if little Ryan loved you so much…maybe the decision for you to come here wasn't his.

What? Maggie and Bill wouldn't have given me up. They knew how much Ryan and I meant to each other!

Did they Harry? Did they really know how much the two of you interacted?

Harry thought long and hard for a moment. *Well…they were never in the room while Ryan and his friends and I played.*

Ester remained silent, but kept an intense stare in her eyes.

But they knew! I'm sure they knew!

Ester continued with her skepticism. *How could they know Harry? If they never witnessed the fun you and Ryan had…how could they have known the bond you two shared?*

Harry scrunched up his face. He didn't want to listen to her words. Instantly, he took a disliking to her. Ester however, pushed on.

Let me ask you something Harry. Did you have a squeaky wheel?

A what?

A squeaky wheel—a wheel that made noise when you ran on it.

Harry immediately closed his eyes, reflecting back on the wheel he loved so much. He thought long and hard. Suddenly he could hear the blissful sounds of his wheel whizzing and squeaking away in his ears. He had always loved that sound. To him, it wasn't noise. To his ears it was like the sweet sounds of music. The more he heard the tunes, the faster he had always peddled.

Harry nodded his head. *I don't know if I would classify it as "squeaky." It was more like listening to Beethoven while exercising!*

Ester immediately rolled her eyes. *That might have been your problem.*

Harry looked at her with confusion. *What are you talking about Ester?*

Face it Harry, we are nocturnal creatures. We sleep during the day and we're active at night. Humans are the exact opposite—they're active during the day and they sleep at night! What you thought was Beethoven's melodies flowing through your ears might have been nothing more than irritating noise to Ryan's parents.

Harry again scrunched up his face. *It never bothered little Ryan!*

Well that may be Harry, but kids are very different than adults. Kids can sleep through anything.

Harry simply looked at her in disbelief. He did not want to believe the words he was hearing. Little did he know that Ester's theory was exactly the reason for the position in which he currently found himself.

What do you know, Ester? What makes you such an expert on the matter?

Because, Harry…that is the reason I am here.

Harry stared at her with wide eyes. Suddenly his sense of self-pity quickly vanished. He hung his head low.

Gosh Ester…I'm so sorry.

Thanks, Harry. It's okay though. I've come to terms with it. I know now that they just weren't the right family for me. I've only been here for a week, but in that short time I've learned that sometimes what you think is right…isn't actually right at all. In time, everything will turn out just fine. I just need to find the "right" family for me. For that, I can wait.

Harry stared at her with blankness in his eyes. He wanted no more of the conversation at hand. He wanted no more to think of little Ryan, Maggie, Bill and the home he would not be going back to. Jumping off of the couch, he headed straight for the wheel attached to the side of the cage. Beethoven…he just wanted Beethoven. With one swift jump he was in the wheel, peddling away, peddling as fast as he could. Trying with all his might, he could not capture the sweet melodies he so longed to hear. The soft, quietness of the wheel offered not one ounce of Beethoven's wonderful sounds. The air carried no melodious tunes. It was a silent whiz of nothingness. He did not want to think. He only wanted the beautiful sounds of melodies long lost.

Two days later, Harry found himself saying good-bye to his new best friend— Butterball. Sitting at the back of his cage, with Ester lying in hers as close to him as she could be, the two of them watched nine-year-old Carla gently stroke Butterball's beautiful blonde fur. They knew instantly by the sparkle in her eyes and the soft sounds of her voice while speaking to him, she would be his new owner. Harry was happy for him, but deep down inside he knew he would miss him. Butterball, with his love for chasing and playing and his keen knack for conversation, had, in just two short days, eliminated Harry's longing for the squeaky wheel he so missed. Now with Butterball gone, Harry would have no one in his cage to distract him from his thoughts.

Geez Ester, that was fast. I've only been here for two days! I was really starting to like him.

I know Harry. But you have to remember, that's what this place is all about—finding new homes for us. We'll all get one; we just have to be patient. Our time will come.

Harry hobbled over to the couch in the corner. Curling up on top of it, he watched Ester walk over to her wheel and get on it. As he closed his eyes he could hear the soft, sweet melody beginning to flow through the air. Instantly he jerked his head up.

Ester was peddling away. Harry immediately jumped off the couch and ran over to the opposite corner of the cage.

Ester…where did that wheel come from? It wasn't making any noise yesterday when you were on it!

Ester stopped peddling and got off the wheel. *It's just a temporary one. The people here put it in here every couple of days while they clean the other one. I'll have my other one back later today.*

No! No! Tell them you want to keep it! It makes noise! It plays Beethoven!

Ester laughed. *No Harry. I don't want to keep this one. The quiet one lets me run on it while people are here looking at us. That is a good thing; people can see that a wheel doesn't have to make noise. And, that way, no one will not want me because I make noise at night! I stand a much better chance of going home with someone that way.*

Harry said nothing while Ester turned around and curled up inside her own little house. With her out of view, Harry hobbled back over to his couch and went to sleep.

In the darkness of the night, Harry awoke to find Ester peddling away on her wheel. He hobbled over to the corner of his cage and sat down. Staring hard at the wheel in her cage, he realized she had been right. The squeaky wheel was now gone, and her old, silent one was back in its place. He sat in total silence watching her peddle away. She seemed happy. She seemed to like its quietness. Glancing over at Lulu, he noticed that she too was running a solo race on her quiet wheel. Just like Ester, she seemed to like the silence. He decided then that he would have to learn to live without Beethoven in his life if he were to ever find a new home. Standing up, he moseyed over to his wheel and climbed on it. Forcing his feet to move, he tried to imagine the sounds he could not hear.

After only a week and a half, Harry had a very welcomed surprise. Three times previously his wheel, couch, and television set had been removed for cleaning, and replaced with others for a short time. He had not once been lucky enough to receive a squeaky wheel like Ester did for a temporary replacement. Today his luck had changed. He watched the hand slowly leave his cage, and then he turned his attention to the wheel. It looked like his old one. With wide eyes and much anticipation, he slowly walked over to it. *Could it be?* Raising one foot in the air, he gently placed it down on the wheel and gave it a small push. It squeaked. Harry's heart jumped for joy. In one swift motion, he jumped onto it and began peddling.

Ester watched him from her cage. She couldn't help but notice the smile on his face. He was in his own little world; listening intently to the tunes that she knew only he could hear. Shaking her head, she slowly closed her eyes.

When Ester awoke, Lulu was in the corner of her cage watching Harry. She glanced in her direction, and then looked over at Harry. He was still on his wheel.

Has he been on that thing this whole time?

Lulu nodded. *Yeah…he just doesn't seem to get tired. He has been going non-stop ever since I started watching him.*

Their conversation was interrupted by the opening of a door. Lulu and Ester glanced over at it, but Harry didn't seem to notice. With his eyes closed, he was still peddling away. He never even heard his cage door open.

"Boy, somebody is sure running up a storm in here, huh little guy?"

Harry abruptly stopped peddling. Looking up he saw the shelter volunteer. She was talking directly to him. He noticed another wheel in her hands. Jumping off, he turned to face her, giving her his best pleading eye look.

Aw…don't take my wheel. I want to keep this one. I like this one.

"Here you go, buddy. Your nice quiet wheel is back, all fresh and clean."

Harry's smile quickly faded. He watched the hand remove the squeaky wheel and sadly allowed the silent one to take its place.

"Okay, you can go back to running now."

I don't want to run anymore. Turning around he went back to his couch and curled up on top of it. He was so tired he didn't even notice how clean it now was. In less than a minute, he had drifted off to sleep.

When Harry finally awoke, he quickly noticed that he had a new roommate. Curled up in the corner of the cage was Teddy, another Teddy Bear hamster just like him. With all four feet sticking straight up in the air, he was snoring away. Edging himself off of the couch, Harry got down and walked up to him. He didn't move. Harry nudged his nose up against his fur. Two eyes suddenly opened.

Hi. I'm Harry. You must be my new roommate.

I'm Teddy. Nice to meet you.

Gee, let me guess. Your owners named you Teddy because you're a Teddy Bear hamster!

Teddy inquisitively looked at Harry. *That's right. How did you know that?*

Harry just smiled at his own wisdom.

Going back to his exercising, Harry had no idea that he would not have time to get to know his new friend. He was clueless that when eight-year-old Brandon entered the room, he had immediately set his sights on him. Running away on his wheel, Harry also did not notice Brandon, standing next to his mother, just a few feet from his cage, staring directly at him. Brandon squeezed his mother's hand tightly.

"Do you see one you like already?" His mother was looking down upon him.

Brandon looked up at her, "Look at that one, mom!" He was pointing directly at Harry. "The coloring is exactly like Honey's!"

Stroking the top of his head, his mother bent down to his level and looked him directly in the eyes.

"Are you sure that you want one who looks just like Honey? Wouldn't you like one with different coloring?"

Brandon had just lost his faithful friend and companion of three years only a month prior. Although he immediately wanted another hamster, his mother insisted on a waiting period before bringing another one home. She was sure that by now he had come to terms with the loss of Honey, but her certainty quickly disappeared as soon as Brandon had pointed out Harry. The similarities between the two were uncanny.

"You know Brandon, you can't replace Honey. This one is a totally different hamster."

With the biggest, bluest eyes, Brandon stared at his mother. The wisdom that she was not yet aware he possessed was quickly revealed in his words.

"I know mom. I wouldn't want to replace her. She was special and unique; no hamster could ever replace her."

Turning his attention back to Harry, he watched him momentarily running on his wheel before focusing his attention back to his mother.

"But that one looks so much like her, it could be her sister or brother—depending on if it's a girl or a boy. It might even be one of her long lost cousins!"

A tear almost found its way down her cheek as Brandon's mom leaned over and hugged her son tightly.

Standing up she turned towards Mary, the rescue volunteer who was assisting them.

"Can we look at that one over there?"

Harry was still peddling away when the door to his cage suddenly opened. As he slowed down his speed, he looked straight up. He almost had to blink twice. Brandon's face was right in the cage opening. Harry quickly shook his head.

Wh...What? The similarities between Brandon and Ryan caused his mind to believe it was playing tricks on him. It took him a few moments to realize that this little boy, although similar in looks and age, was not his long lost little Ryan. *Wait a minute...you're not Ryan!*

Staring deep into Harry's beady, black eyes, Brandon immediately felt some kind of connection. He wasn't sure what it was, but there was something about the little hamster staring back at him that instantly made up his mind. Reaching into the cage, he brought Harry close up to his heart. Gently stroking his head, he looked directly up at his mother.

"This is the one, mom. I'm sure of it."

Mary offered the only words she knew of his presence at the rescue shelter.

"This little guy is Harry. He was surrendered to us by a family who had a little boy around your same age."

Brandon's face immediately lit up with a smile. His gleaming eyes pleaded with his mother.

"Can we get him mom, can we? This is the one. This is the one I want."

Smiling with extreme pride over the maturity of her son, his mother could do nothing more than shake her head. Turning her attention to Mary, she spoke softly.

"We'd like to adopt this one."

harry the hamster

ONE MAN'S TRASH IS ANOTHER MAN'S TREASURE

Brandon was very well versed in bringing home a new small companion animal. He had read all the books and studied up on the best interests of his pet before he first got Honey. Clearly, he was a very responsible pet owner. He knew he should already have Harry's new home completely set up before introducing him to it. Not wanting to have any of Honey's things around as reminders for Brandon, his parents had packed away her things and placed them in storage, awaiting their next garage sale. So, when the decision was made to bring home another new pet, a shopping spree was definitely in the making. A wonderful, blue, two-story cage equipped with a nice, quiet wheel, matching food and water dishes sat in Brandon's room, awaiting the new arrival.

Brandon and his parents had set up the cage the day before Harry was to arrive at their home. Brandon was thrilled with the colorful wheel that attached directly to the side of the cage. It provided more floor space for his next pet to run around in. The food and water bowls were placed strategically on the

33

bottom of the cage, while fresh new bedding blanketed the gray flooring. To make his next pet feel even more at home, pencil-shaped chew sticks were placed on both levels, along with two blue igloo hide-a-homes. And, as if that wasn't enough, a package of yogurt treats lay on the kitchen counter, awaiting their fate.

Brandon had been adamant about the next companion animal to enter their home. Through his bond with Honey, his connection to the animal world had become filled with love and compassion. After seeing so many reports on television about homeless pets, mostly consisting of dogs and cats, he was compelled to seek out any agency that had small animals available for adoption. During his research, he had been totally surprised to discover how many of the little critters of the world sailed in the same ships. And, through their many conversations with him during his month-long waiting period, even his parents had been quite impressed when they learned the details of where their next pet would come from. Brandon was the one who had discovered Critter Heaven Small Animal Rescue. They could not argue with his compassion.

Harry was nervous traveling in the box. He peered out the holes in the side, listening intently to the sounds of the cars passing by. He remembered those sounds. They brought back memories of his travel to the shelter. He had no idea back then that his ride in a car would be to abandon him. His mind could not remember the first time he'd ever ridden in a car. He was much too young. That had been the ride when he first found his home with Ryan. Although he was keenly aware that he was now going to another new home, he was still extremely apprehensive. There were no guarantees that this time would be forever and he did not like the sounds of traveling. Through one of the small holes in the box, one of his eyes could see Brandon sitting in the seat next to him. That was the only thing that gave him a sense of comfort.

Harry was introduced to his new home and then left alone to ponder his new surroundings. He watched Brandon and his parents leave the room, silently grateful that he had time alone. He needed to absorb everything that was happening without any interruption. His eyes marveled at the height of the second level. Cautiously he walked up the ramp, surveying the entire cage with every step. There was no television set, no couch like in his home at the adoption facility, but this place had everything else. There was a wheel, two igloos, chew sticks galore, and fresh food and water. He was extremely fascinated. If he was tired, he had a wonderful igloo to escape to on the bottom level, and one on the top should he ever need to hide. His new place even had a tube that would allow him to climb in and crawl up to reach a nesting place at the very top of the house. He could burrow in so many different places and at several different heights.

Harry had been wandering around and inspecting for almost an hour before he finally got tired. Curling up on the second level, he stuck his feet straight up in the air and drifted off to sleep. He hadn't realized that two hours had passed when Brandon walked into the room and straight up to his cage.

"Hi there, Harry. Are you liking your new home?"

One hand reached in and gently petted him on the head. Harry was so content, he worried that Brandon would take him out of his cage. He didn't want to play; he didn't want to be hugged. Not right at that point. He only wanted a little more time to adapt to his new surroundings. Little did he know, Brandon understood his thoughts all too well. With several gentle strokes to his head, Brandon turned around and left. Harry watched in silence as he exited the room. With the room totally silent, a smile formed on Harry's lips. *Gosh…he really does understand!*

There had been a very unique bond between Brandon and Harry when they first met, but neither one of them knew just how deep that bond really was until about three weeks after their initial meeting. The two of them played together constantly. Harry received so much more attention than he could have ever anticipated from his new home. But late one night, fate would step in and make its mark. In the early morning hours, when everyone should have been fast asleep, Brandon suddenly stirred in his sleep. Within minutes, he woke up. Instantly his eyes drifted over to Harry's cage. As should be the norm for a creature such as Harry, he was peddling away on his wheel. Brandon stared at his face. It looked intent, but it didn't look happy. He reflected back to the days when Honey would peddle on her wheel, for hours on end, into the wee hours of the morning. It would wake him up, but those sweet sounds of her squeaky wheel were always accompanied by a big, wide smile. After watching her for several minutes, he would easily drift back off to sleep. The squeaking noise brought him a sense of peace. He missed that old wheel. He couldn't help but wonder if Harry had had one that he missed as well.

The next morning, Brandon had no problem in approaching the subject with his parents.

"Mom, can we get Honey's old wheel out of the garage?"

His mother was clearly confused by his request.

"Why do you want her wheel, Brandon? It's old and squeaky! Besides, it used to wake you up half the time. Your new hamster has everything he could possibly need, and, might I add, his wheel is quiet."

"But that is the problem, mom! I don't hear his silent wheel!"

His father raised his eyebrows. "You want to hear that noise at night?"

Brandon nodded his head. "Yeah dad, I do. I know it wakes me up sometimes, but that noise always gave me a sense of comfort when I would try to go back to sleep. I remember I used to sit up sometimes and watch Honey running on it. She always seemed to be having the time of her life. When I'd roll over and lay back down, that noise helped me drift back off to sleep. It's like the noise let me know she was happy."

His mother looked over at his father, but said nothing.

Brandon, amidst the silence, decided not to further the conversation with his observation of Harry's intent look the previous night. He already felt a little embarrassed by his own words. He did not want to mention Honey's hamster smile.

When Brandon returned home from school, he ran straight up to his room to see Harry. As soon as he opened the cage, Harry popped his head out from hiding and peered at him with one eye.

Hey Brandon! His eyes seemed to sparkle with delight.

Brandon took him out of his cage and set him down on the floor. The two chased each other around the room for almost an hour. Harry almost seemed to giggle as he ran under the bed. Brandon noticed that Harry seemed to have a new air about him, but he couldn't pinpoint the reasoning. He just seemed to have a new spark.

Long into the early morning hours, Brandon's eyes suddenly burst open. He found himself staring at the window. He tilted his ear to the left. He could not ignore the noise. Bolting straight up, he threw his legs over the edge of the bed. Looking directly at the cage, he could barely see Harry in the darkness, but there was no mistaking that sound. Harry was peddling so fast on the wheel that Brandon thought he might injure himself. And, the wheel squeaked a little louder with each step Harry took.

Rubbing his eyes, Brandon quietly got up and walked over to Harry's cage. The big silent wheel was still attached to the side, but off in the corner on the bottom of the cage sat Honey's old, squeaky wheel. He momentarily watched Harry peddling away on it.

"When did my mom put that in there Harry?" He could not believe he hadn't noticed it when he took Harry out of the cage earlier. Lost in his own little world, Harry suddenly stopped peddling, but did not get off the wheel. He looked straight up at Brandon and deep into his eyes. Brandon was positive he smiled. Quickly turning his attention back to the wheel, he started to peddle again.

Brandon returned to his bed. Curling up under the covers, he drifted back to sleep with a deep sense of peace and a smile of his own that spread across his entire face. The squeakiness echoed throughout the room as Harry listened once again to the wonderful, sweet sounds of Beethoven.

cindy the chinchilla

CHAPTER TWO

cindy the chinchilla

THE IMPORTANCE OF LOVE

Cindy stirred in her cage the minute Gabby entered the room. She knew what was about to happen. But, before those feet could come charging at her again, she ran and hid in the corner of her cage. She didn't even have time to notice Gabby wasn't alone.

"Look! Come over here, Marci!" The voice was as high-pitched as the last time that same sentence was spoken.

"Look at my new pet!"

Ripping open the cage door, Gabby's arm rustled around in the cage before it fell upon silky fur.

"Come on Cindy, come out! There's someone who wants to see you!"

Cindy felt the hand press hard against her body. She did not try to fight it.

She allowed herself to be picked up and then quickly burrowed her head into Gabby's arms.

"Isn't she just adorable?"

Marci tilted her head and tried to see Cindy's face. "What is it?"

"It's a chinchilla!" Gabby boasted proudly. "She comes from somewhere in South America, Peru or Chile—somewhere around there. "Isn't she cool looking?"

"She looks like an oversized squirrel with big ears."

Gabby pulled Cindy away from her body and held her up for Marci to see.

"Wow, she really has a cute face."

Gabby kissed Cindy on the head and placed her back in her cage. Cindy immediately ran back and hid in the corner. After closing the door, Gabby and Marci left the room.

When silence returned to the room and Cindy was sure the coast was clear, she came out from her hiding spot and perched herself up on the ledge attached to the side of her cage. Closing her eyes she drifted back off to sleep.

Cindy had only been at her new home for two short weeks, but she already knew she didn't like it. She was tired of constantly being classified as "unique," "different" and "cool-looking." In her eyes she was a normal chinchilla. She certainly didn't look any different than any other chinchilla in the world, so she wasn't sure what the fascination with her looks was all about. She had been quite excited the first few days after her arrival—a new home, a wonderful cage, lots of toys and plenty of food, hay and water—but she quickly realized that those *things* were what her new home was all about. The only time she had been picked up was to be shown off. There were no loving arms for her to snuggle in, very few cooing words spoken to her and not once had she had the freedom to run free from her cage. Discouraged, she sat on her perch and wondered if life was always going to be this way.

Gabby had been ecstatic when her parents decided she was old enough, and responsible enough, to get a pet of her very own. She picked the chinchilla hands down. Many of her other friends at school had pets, but none of them had a chinchilla. Her parents had paid for the primary home and necessities, but Gabby used her own allowance money to buy extra toys and treats. She was going to be sure to lavish her new pet with lots of extras.

Gabby had impressed her parents with her commitment to her new responsibilities. Cindy's cage was cleaned almost every day before school. Fresh water and fresh food were placed in her bowls every morning. She had been unwavering about not allowing her new pet to get any kind of illness from bacteria. She had read all the information about the importance of a clean cage, the proper vegetable diet, and the items that were necessary to satisfy her pet's gnawing habit. But, what she failed to read or realize, was *the importance of love*.

Cindy was slowly beginning to lose weight. The stress of her unhappy environment was beginning to take its toll on her. At first, Gabby did not seem to notice. It was into Cindy's fifth week as Gabby's "unique" and "cool-looking" pet that her idol status came crashing down. By now, everyone at school knew of Cindy, the "unusual" pet. She had been handled by more kids than she cared to count. Little Suzie however, had no idea how fragile Cindy's tiny body was. As soon as Gabby handed her over, Suzie squeezed her too tightly. Unbeknownst to either of them, she had cracked one of Cindy's ribs. Crying out in pain, Cindy quickly turned and bit her.

"Ow! That hurt!" Suzie's cries were almost as loud as Cindy's. She shoved her back towards Gabby. "She bit me!"

Gabby looked sternly at Cindy, "What a bad girl you are!" Placing her directly back into her cage, she attended to the needs of her friend.

The next morning Gabby awoke to find Cindy lying openly in the corner of her cage. She did not try to run and hide when Gabby opened the cage door. Gabby stared at her momentarily. She somehow looked skinnier than she did before. Reaching in, she tried to arouse her. Cindy stared up at her, but did not move. Suddenly fear set in. Gabby darted for the door screaming for her mother.

"Mom! Mom, come quick! I think Gabby is sick!"

That day at school proved to be quite difficult for Gabby. She could not concentrate on her studies. She stared at the teacher, listening to his every word, but absorbing none of what he was saying. All she could think about was Cindy. After dropping her off at school, her mother had taken Cindy directly to the vet. She closed her eyes and visualized little Cindy lying on a table, the vet poking at her from every side. Suddenly, it hit her. For the five short weeks she had

had her, Gabby had lavished Cindy with everything she could think of that her allowance would allow. The one thing she hadn't thought to give her was love. The two of them had no special connection. They shared no bond. Suddenly, her heart ached inside. Her thoughts drifted to the relationship she shared with her own parents. They didn't have a lot of money. They couldn't give her everything that some of the other girls at school had, but what they did give her was love. Every night, whether they were watching a movie while eating popcorn or playing Scrabble at the kitchen table, they shared great moments. She always felt secure. She always felt loved. At that very moment, Gabby decided that she would spend more time with Cindy. She promised herself she would take her out of her cage, hold her, and play with her. No longer would Cindy be an object to be shown off to her friends. She would be a member of their family. Just the thought of Cindy lying in her arms while watching television made her smile. Little did she know her newly-found compassion was just a little too late. She would never be given the opportunity to hold Cindy again.

On the bus ride home from school, Gabby said not a word. Her ears could hear the conversations of the other kids chatting away, but she remained silent. She couldn't wait to burst through the door, run to her room and check on Cindy. She pictured a bandage around her leg, a dressing across her head, a tiny body cast around her belly. She had no idea what had happened at the vet that day, but she knew Cindy would need her. She would not invite any friends over; she wouldn't even answer the phone. Cindy would need her full attention, and that, she was totally prepared to give her. What she wasn't prepared for was what she would find when she entered her bedroom.

Bursting through her bedroom door, Gabby ran directly up to Cindy's cage. It was empty. Her heart immediately sank. Quickly she looked at her watch. She could not call her mother at work, by now she was already on her way home. Gabby went into the living room and paced the floor, looking at the clock every few seconds.

"Come on, mom. Hurry up and get home!"

When her mother arrived home from work, Gabby instantly met her at the door.

"Where's Cindy? Is she still at the vet? What's wrong with her?"

With a look of sadness, her mother placed her arm around her shoulder and led her back into the living room.

"Gabby, come on. We need to talk."

Fear took total control of every vein in Gabby's body. "Mom, she's okay isn't she? Please tell me she's okay!"

"Honey, Cindy is going to be just fine."

Sitting down on the sofa, her mother turned to face her.

"Gabby, Cindy is not well right now but, the good news is that in time, she should be okay."

A tear gently fell from Gabby's eyes. "What's wrong with her mom? When will she be coming home?"

"Gabby, she won't be coming home."

"What do you mean? You just said she'd be okay!"

Gabby's mom had thought long and hard that day about how difficult the conversation she had to have with her daughter that afternoon would be, but she didn't realize how hard until that very moment. In the five weeks they had had Cindy, she had not once seen in Gabby anything that would constitute the emotions she was now displaying. She had witnessed the pride in her voice when she spoke of Cindy, seen how much she loved to show her off to her friends, but she had never seen any signs of the love and compassion that was now being revealed.

"Cindy has lost some weight honey. The vet thinks that it's probably due to stress. But on top of that, she has a cracked rib."

"What?" Gabby wiped the small tear from her eye.

"Right now Gabby, Cindy needs a lot of medical treatment. She has to stay in the hospital for close to a week. The vet bills are going to be very expensive. It's just something we cannot afford right now."

"We can't just leave her in pain mom! She has to be fixed. She has to be made well again!"

"She will, Gabby, she will. That's what I'm trying to tell you. We cannot afford the vet bills, but the hospital will give her the treatment she needs."

"They're going to do that for free?"

"No honey, they're not. I had to surrender Cindy to them. They will take care of her and make her better. They will pay that cost, but in turn, we can't bring her back here. Once she is well, they will send her somewhere to find another home."

Gabby instantly burst into tears. Her mother squeezed her shoulder tightly.

"You have to remember Gabby that the important thing is that she gets well. We may not be able to get her back, but after she is well, she will find a good home. Know in your heart that she is going to be okay in the end. That is all that should matter."

Gabby went to sleep that night with a broken heart, but also with a newly-found sense of knowledge. Her thoughts and prayers were with Cindy. She had to keep her faith that she would be okay and that, in time, she would find a new home that already had the one thing that she had just discovered—animals, just like people, need love and attention. In time she would ask her parents to bring another pet into their home. And, when that time came, she promised her heart that she would heed the lessons she had learned.

Cindy lay in a small kennel at the vet hospital. She was in some pain, but she was also surrounded by a new sense of wonder. She had no idea who half the people in the room with her were, but she wasn't bothered by them in the least. Not once since her arrival had anyone come charging at her cage. Every hand that had reached inside had been slow. Every touch she received was gentle. No one had grabbed her or pulled her with force. Voices spoke softly to her, and then faded away. She reveled in the peaceful surroundings. Her stress had completely vanished.

Cindy's new environment had been an added plus to her speedy recovery. She was relaxed and happy, and her injuries healed faster than even her vet had anticipated. Within only a matter of a few short weeks, she was ready to be moved to a new place that would aid in finding her a permanent home. Cindy was ready for the challenge.

The ride in the car was a peaceful one. Cindy enjoyed the quietness around her. She wrapped herself up in the security of the darkness, finding comfort amongst the four cardboard walls that surrounded her. Somehow she had known the hospital would not be her permanent home. She wasn't sure how she knew it—she just knew. Now she was keenly aware that she was going somewhere new, although she had no idea where. It didn't matter to her anyway. She hadn't seen Gabby or her mother for a long time. Inside she knew she wasn't going back to their home. She hadn't felt fear or stress for as long as she could remember and she was happy keeping it that way.

Once they arrived at the Critter Heaven Small Animal Rescue, Cindy was immediately placed into a cage with two other female chinchillas. She instantly welcomed the company of others her own size.

Hi! My name is Cindy!

Pearl and Magnolia both looked at her with inquisitive eyes. Neither had expected any newcomers to their cage, even though it was large enough to handle many more chinchillas than just the two of them. They were not as eager as Cindy to make new friends. They both had arrived at the rescue shelter within days of each other and that was just over two months ago. Obviously, the two were now very close.

Magnolia glanced over at Pearl, and then focused her attention back to Cindy. She decided she would be the spokesperson.

Uh…hi. I'm Magnolia. This is my friend Pearl.

Nice to meet both of you! Cindy's eyes were glistening.

Why do you look so happy Cindy? Don't you know what this place is?

I think I do! It's a place where I'm going to find a new home right?

Right, Magnolia answered. *And that makes you happy?*

Well of course it does. Cindy made herself comfortable on the soft bedding that lay beneath her. *I don't have a home and I want one. Where could a better place to be than here?*

Didn't you come from a home?

No, well…sort of. I had a home once, but I came here from a hospital.

For the first time, Pearl spoke up. *Oh my gosh, a hospital? What happened?*

Cindy proceeded to explain her situation. She recounted her story of constantly being handled by a lot of children, being shown off to everyone, and how she quickly became the idolization of all of Gabby's school friends.

Wow! They idolized you? That must have been fascinating!

Actually it wasn't! Cindy, by the look on her face, obviously didn't share Pearl's same sentiments. *You wouldn't like it either if you were constantly referred to as "unusual" or were constantly being dragged out of your cage, handled too roughly and being shown off to a gazillion different people! That's what caused my cracked rib!*

Magnolia instantly thought about her past home. She missed it terribly. She could easily envision herself sitting on the bed with Jackson, curled up in his arm while he did his homework. That wonderful, sensational feeling of contentment she shared with him. She remembered how she would slowly lift up her head and look at him. His nose would still be buried in his books. Slowly she would inch her way up to his face and, with her nose almost pressed against his cheek, she would stare him down. As soon as he felt her eyes, he immediately closed his book and laughed. Picking her up, he would lie back against his pillow, place her on his chest and whisper sweet words in her ear while gently stroking her fur.

Cindy instantly noticed a tear start to form in her eyes.

Are you okay, Magnolia?

Looking over at her, the fondness returned to her eyes. *Yes, Cindy, I'm fine.*

I'm sorry. I didn't mean to bring up any old memories.

It's okay. I know Jackson had to go off to college. He would have taken me if he could, but I wasn't allowed in the dormitories. I know he misses me just as much as I miss him.

Cindy remained silent. She looked over at Pearl. She too seemed to have a look of fondness in her eyes.

Is that why you're here Pearl? Did your owner go off to college too?

Pearl shook her tiny head. *No. In my case, Danielle got married. Her husband has all kinds of issues with allergies. They couldn't have pets of any kind. It's okay though. I understood. We had a great two years together!*

Two years? You had an owner for two years?

Well, I was with Jackson for three, Magnolia added.

How long were you with yours?

Cindy hung her head. *I was only there for five weeks.*

Pearl and Magnolia both inched their way over to Cindy. The resentment they felt upon her arrival quickly disappeared. Now they wanted to do nothing more than offer her words of encouragement. At least the two of them had once had great homes with loving owners. That was something Cindy had not yet experienced. They wanted to give her hope.

You'll like this place Cindy, really you will. The people here are all so nice. And you wouldn't believe how many people come here. This place finds so many new homes for us animals!

Yeah Cindy, Magnolia's right. I'm so sorry you weren't happy in your last home, but have no doubts—you'll find a new one soon!

Cindy almost seemed to smile. *So, how long have you two been here?*

Without thinking, Magnolia was quick to answer. *We've been together here for almost two months.*

Two months? I thought you said a lot of animals get homes in here. Why have you been here for that long?

Magnolia suddenly wished she had not answered the question. Pearl could read her thoughts. Like the true friend she was, she instantly stepped in.

One thing you have to realize Cindy is that there are a lot of very young children that come in here looking for a pet. This place is great at adopting animals out, but the people here are very concerned with the animals themselves. You're one of us, so you know that we like very soft voices—no loud screaming—we're fragile, and sometimes it takes us a while to trust. You know how our fear levels are. It took me almost three months to trust Danielle, and I have to admit, she had to work at it for a long time. One thing she definitely had was patience.

Yeah, Magnolia added. *You yourself said you were injured because no one knew how fragile you are. Just think—if someone had grabbed you by your tail, it could have come off!*

Cindy shuddered at the thought of losing her tail.

This place is pretty strict about getting us homes. They turn down any adoption they feel isn't the right environment for us. We've been looked at a lot, just not allowed to go home with anyone so far.

Pearl's last statement made perfect sense. Visions of her past home quickly flashed through Cindy's mind. She did not want to find another home as such.

Well, then that's okay. As long as you say this is a good place, I'll be happy here until I find a permanent home of my own!

Along with Cindy's arrival to the shelter came fate. Only a short week later, Tom and Nancy visited the shelter in hopes of adopting a chinchilla. Having had chinchillas previously, they already knew how to properly care for them. Their screening was a short one, and they were instantly approved. However, the decision of which chinchilla to adopt would not be based on an instant connection, as they were both very familiar with the time and patience it took to gain the trust of a chinchilla. They had no preference to size, color or gender. Their choice would be based solely on time. They would adopt the one chinchilla that had been at the shelter the longest. Unbeknownst to either of them, a decision would still have to be made as both Pearl and Magnolia had been at the center for two months.

Out in the hallway the conversation was short. After learning about the backgrounds of both Pearl and Magnolia, hearing about how close the two had become and already knowing the importance of companionship amongst animals, the choice was crystal clear. Tom and Nancy would become the proud parents of not one, but two chinchillas—Pearl *and* Magnolia.

Cindy was extremely happy for Pearl and Magnolia, but she wondered how she would feel in a couple of days when the loneliness of not having her friends around would sink in. Gracie, however, would not give her the opportunity to find out. Fate's presence in the rescue shelter was still hovering.

It had only been a month since Gracie lost her little Lola. Her other chinchilla, Candy, was not adjusting as well as she had hoped. It was evident she missed her friend dearly. Gracie knew it was time. Candy needed a new friend. Just as with her other chinchillas, adoption was the only answer. That exact same day, only a few hours after Tom and Nancy had walked out with Pearl and Magnolia, Gracie walked into the Critter Heaven Small Animal Rescue. That same day, only a few short hours after Pearl and Magnolia went to their new home, Cindy found hers.

cindy the chinchilla

BEAUTY ISN'T ONLY SKIN DEEP

Cindy remained very quiet on the ride to her new home. Gracie drove in silence, the radio turned down, her mind lost in the stillness of the atmosphere. She continually tried to imagine what it was like for Cindy at her prior home. She could not phantom how she had incurred the injuries that she had. None of the volunteers at the rescue shelter had been able to give her any information about her past, except for the fact that she had been surrendered to the hospital because the prior owner could not afford the vet bills for those injuries. She had no idea Cindy was only in her previous home for five weeks before visiting the hospital. When she was holding her at the shelter before signing the paperwork, she could sense a certain insecurity about her. She seemed a bit shy, but she showed no signs of fear. It was almost as if she was happy she was going somewhere else, even if she had no idea where that place would be. Gracie could only imagine that her prior home was not a happy one.

She reached over and softly petted the box where Cindy quietly sat.

"Don't you worry little one. It'll take time, but I'm sure you'll enjoy your new home."

If Gracie had been worried about how Candy was going to react to first meeting a new friend, her concerns quickly vanished the minute she introduced the two of them. Cuddling Cindy in her arms, she bent down and leaned into Candy's cage. Candy immediately jumped off her perch and walked up to her. Giving her an inquisitive look, she then focused her attention on Cindy. Cindy was staring directly at her.

Cindy showed no hesitation. She leaned forward, almost as if she was trying to sniff Candy's nose.

Hi! Who are you?

Hi! I'm Candy. Who are you?

My name is Cindy.

Candy looked up at her mom. Smiling, Gracie allowed Cindy to jump from her arms and into the cage.

"It's okay, Candy. Say hello. This is your new friend."

Candy turned around to look at Cindy. She did not seem the least bit bothered that a new chinchilla was in her cage. It had been very lonely since Lola left. She welcomed the company.

Gracie leaned back on her heels and watched the two of them discover each other. After sitting there for almost thirty minutes, she saw no signs of aggression, no signs of fear, and no signs of jealousy or resentment. It was almost as if they were two people meeting on the street for the first time, having a casual conversation. She could easily sense that both of them had a void in life and that each one could fill the void with the other. She was keenly aware that they too could sense that same feeling.

"This is so perfect!" Gracie's squeal was a quiet whisper.

The next evening when Gracie returned home from work, Candy and Cindy were both nestled together on the highest perch in the cage. When she slowly pulled open the door to the cage, their eyes immediately opened.

"Come on girls! Time to roam!"

Gracie stood up and walked away into the kitchen. Candy immediately jumped off the perch and darted out of the cage onto the living room floor. Cindy remained in place on the perch. Stopping just short of the cage door, Candy turned around and looked at Cindy.

Come on, silly. It's time to play!

Cindy hesitated. *But you're outside of the cage!*

Well, yeah. Gracie's home. It's time to play and snuggle!

Cindy appeared confused. *What does that mean? Play and snuggle? Aren't we supposed to stay in the cage?*

Candy looked at her curiously. *What? We only stay in the cage when mom's at work. Other than that we get to roam around, lie on her lap while watching television and snuggle in her arms! Haven't you ever done that before?*

Still on the perch, Cindy could only shake her head.

Oh boy! You haven't even begun to experience love and fun! Come on.

Still Cindy hesitated.

Candy walked back to the open door of the cage and sat down in front of it. *Come on Cindy, you'll see. Trust me. Come on!*

Cindy slowly jumped off the perch and walked over to the door of the cage. Cautiously she stuck one foot outside of it. Staring around the room, she could not believe the wide-open space in front of her. Suddenly she smiled.

Really, Candy? We get all this area to run around in?

Candy shook her head. *Yeah, and wait until you see the second bedroom of the apartment. It's basically all set up for us. You think the two perches in the cage are great—you haven't seen anything yet! We have all kinds of height in there to jump on.*

Cindy slowly followed Candy into the other room. Her eyes reveled at the sights in front of her. *All of this is for us?*

Yeah. This is where we'll normally be when mom's asleep. She knows we like to stay up all night, so this is where we hang out so we don't disturb her.

You mean we don't have to stay in the cage while she's sleeping?

No, of course not!

But we were in there last night.

That's probably because it was your first night here, that's all. I know my mom. I'm sure she just wanted you to get used to the new place.

Cindy's eyes refocused themselves on the many different levels of perches in front of her. Immediately she squealed as she ran as fast as her feet could take her and jumped onto the first one she could reach. She turned around and faced Candy, starring at her in complete awe.

This is soooo unbelievable!

Candy laughed, and then ran and jumped on a perch of her own.

Cindy had no idea how much time had passed since she and Candy had entered the "chinchilla room." Gracie had already finished dinner, cleaned up the dishes and changed into her pajamas. Sitting on the couch, the television tuned to a movie, she called out to them.

"Candy! Cindy! Come on girls! Time to watch television!"

Cindy turned to face Candy at the sound of the voice coming from the other room.

Come on, Cindy! Now we get to curl up with mom on the couch!

Cindy had no idea what that meant, but she automatically knew it had to be something good.

Candy darted out of the room with Cindy following right at her feet. In one flying leap she landed on the couch, right next to Gracie's leg. This time Cindy did not hesitate. Gracie reached over and gently stroked the fur of both of them.

"Okay, you guys get comfortable."

Candy immediately burrowed herself into the crook of Gracie's arm, and then glanced back at Cindy.

Come on, curl up with us.

Cindy cocked her head to one side. *That's okay? She's not going to get mad?*

Are you kidding? She loves this as much as I do! Come on!

Gracie cautiously watched the actions of her two girls. She could almost swear that they were having a private conversation. She could definitely sense Cindy's reservations.

"Come on Cindy, it's okay." Softly, she patted the empty spot next to Candy.

Cindy slowly raised her head and stared directly at her. There was a sweet, soft glow glistening in her eyes. Taking cautious steps, she slowly inched her way up next to Candy, burrowing her head in her fur. She welcomed the tender, warm touch of Gracie's hand gently rustling her fur.

Candy smiled. *See, I told you it was okay.*

After several minutes of watching the movie, Gracie allowed her eyes to drift down upon the two silky furred bodies that lay next to her. She smiled at the contentment on both of their faces. She knew she had made the right decision in adopting Cindy.

"Soon you are going to absolutely love it here Cindy," she whispered.

Cindy understood her words, although Gracie could not understand hers.

I already do, mom…I already do.

reggie the rat

CHAPTER THREE

reggie the rat

LOOKING FOR BILLY

Reggie scurried through the open field of grass and dirt, letting his little nose take him around in circles. Even as far as he had traveled, he still could not find anything, nothing at all, that looked familiar to him. For a rat, who did not know the meaning of the word "lost," that's exactly what he was. He never dreamed that sneaking out of his cage and hiding from Billy's mom as he ran along the baseboards of the walls would put him in the predicament in which he now found himself. He had no idea that one baseboard would lead him right out the open front door. Engrossed in the newness of the green shrubbery, he never saw Billy's mom walk back into the house and shut the door. However, the minute he noticed the opening wasn't there any longer, he quickly realized his little game of hide and seek was over.

The sun was shinning brilliantly. Reggie was accustomed to the differences between light and dark, but only the light that light bulbs produced. He had caught glimpses of the actual sun before, shining in through Billy's window, but he had never once felt the true heat it could bring down on his tiny body. He needed to find some shade. He needed somewhere cool and secure to sleep. Venturing further and further away from the house, he finally found what he was looking for. Burying himself amongst a nice pile of leaves, he gently closed his eyes.

When Reggie finally awoke, it was pitch dark. The darkness gave him a huge sense of security. Nighttime was his time. In the black of the night, while everyone in the house was fast asleep, he was up roaming around his cage, peddling on his wheel and living his silent dream of winning the National Rat Peddling Contest in his head.

Amidst the quietness that surrounded him, his thoughts instantly fell to Billy. He could easily imagine the state of panic Billy would be in when he returned home from school only to discover he wasn't in his cage. He knew how much Billy adored him. His heart could sense the devastation Billy would suffer when he saw the empty cage. Once Billy noticed the open bars that he had chewed through, he would, without a doubt, run all over the house, desperately searching for him. That image of Billy brought tears to his eyes. Suddenly he was pained with guilt. He shouldn't have chewed through those bars. *Why did I do that? What if Billy thinks I didn't want to be there anymore…didn't love him anymore…or didn't want to share my life with him anymore?* Those thoughts were too much for him to bear. Instantly he knew what he had to do. He had to find his way back to Billy. He wasn't sure how he was going to do it, but he had to find him. Stretching out his little front legs, he yawned, got up, and started on his journey.

Living in a cage, roaming around the four squared walls of Billy's bedroom, and being an ornament attached to Billy's shoulder while watching television did not help Reggie one bit in his quest for understanding directions. His little mind could not grasp the concepts of North, South, East and West. Additionally, having his nose constantly sniffing the ground as he trudged through the night only served to lead him further and further away from the house he once knew, and deeper and deeper into lost territory. By morning, there was no going back. He simply had no idea of where he was. With the sun beating down on his little body again, he surrendered to the depression that wanted to take over. Finding another cool and secure place in which to sleep, he buried himself from the world, closed his eyes, and tried desperately to block everything from his mind. Despite a valiant effort, he found no success. Although shaded from the heat of the sun, his little body tossed and turned, flip-flopped left and flip-flopped right, trying to erase the thoughts of Billy that kept popping into his head. If he had never realized the true, deep love and compassion he had for that little boy before, he could not help but realize it now. He desperately wanted to be in his cage, peddling away on his wheel, lost in his dreams of winning the race, while the soft, gentle snoring sounds of Billy rang throughout the room.

The darkness of night brought a new companion into Reggie's life. While on his search for Billy once again, he instantly froze at the sound of leaves rustling only a few feet from him. With his nose to the sky, he called out softly. *Who's out there?*

The air remained silent for only a brief moment before words were returned to him.

Who is asking? Who are you? What are you doing here?

Reggie instantly recognized the tone, but did not recognize the voice. His keen instincts told him it was a member of his rodent family, but not a close family member. He knew it was a rat, but he also recognized the fact that it wasn't a rat such as himself.

I'm Reggie…who are you?

I'm Arnold. What are you doing so close to my family? What do you want?

Reggie instantly perked up. His mind held fast to the word family. With quick, short visions, he pictured two-legged creatures amongst them.

Your family?

Yes, my family. Joan, my wife, and our three sons are right here. Why are you so close to us and what is it you want?

A long sigh came from deep within Reggie's throat, but Arnold could not hear it.

I'm sorry, Reggie replied, *I have a family too, but they are not of the same kind as us. I'm just lost. I'm trying to find my way back to them. I mean you no harm.*

Arnold, too, could recognize the tone, but like Reggie, he did not recognize the voice. He was a bit curious as to the mention of a family, but extremely intrigued by Reggie's use of the words "same kind as us." With extreme caution, he ventured forward, allowing his nose to be seen amidst the darkness. With one quick glance back at his wife and sons, Arnold turned to look at Reggie.

Face to face, the two rats stared at each other. Both seemed to share a bond, but at the same time, both felt the differences that were so apparent. The silence seemed endless, as they looked deep into each other's eyes. Finally, feeling somewhat comfortable, Arnold spoke.

What do you mean, you have a family but not as the same kind as us?

Reggie instantly burst into a grin at the first thought of Billy. He could not wait to tell Arnold all about the little boy who changed his life after he had selected him from the cage at the pet store. With stars shining brilliantly from his eyes, Reggie proceeded to tell Arnold about the wonderful, two-legged creatures of the world who had hearts of gold and souls full of love and compassion. His speech rambled on about his endless evenings sitting on Billy's shoulder, having his fur softly stroked while the family watched television, and the games of chase he and Billy played in his room before he went to bed. Arnold's head tilted sideways as Reggie described the wheel he ran on every night and his wild dreams to one day win the National Rat Peddling Contest.

Arnold was completely flabbergasted. He could not believe the interaction Reggie had had with humans. The only contact he had had with the two-legged creatures of the world was the fast-paced foot race he had participated in to avoid the hands that wanted to catch him and send him to an early death. He simply could not believe Reggie's words.

It's true—I tell you—it's true! There are actually people out there who love us… even though we are rats! Billy is one of them! You wouldn't believe the bond that we have. I really did sit on his shoulder all the time.

An instant sense of loneliness plagued Reggie's eyes. Although Arnold didn't recognize or understand what it meant, he could tell something was happening deep inside his newly-found friend's little soul. He wanted to offer comfort, but he didn't know how. He did not understand the feelings that Reggie was having.

You are more than welcome to come and live with us.

Reggie smiled. *Thanks. I would like to spend some time with you and meet your family, but after that, I must move on. I have to find Billy.*

Reggie enjoyed the time he spent with Arnold and his family. It was the first happiness he'd experienced since he wandered away from his home. He was very intrigued by the life they led. He admired the fact that they had to fend for themselves to survive, something he had never had to do—that is, until he got lost. He did not share the same sense of self-satisfaction that they felt when food was discovered. For him it was merely a survival task that only brought back memories of his food dish back in his cage that was always fresh, and always full. He could see the sparkle in Arnold's eyes when he spoke of Joan as well as when he recanted stories of the funny things the boys did. He could also feel the enormous sense of pride Arnold had for his family through his words.

The conversation that evening taught Reggie an important lesson. The loving arms of Billy and the security of his own two-legged family was enough. There was no longer a need inside of him to escape or to venture out into unknown territory. He suddenly realized what a great life he had, and what he had lost. He vowed that evening that if he ever did find his way back to Billy, he would appreciate every, single moment with him. He would never stray again.

The conversation and laughter lasted until the early hours of the morning. Reggie could not believe that he had passed yet another night without running on his wheel. He wondered if Arnold and his family would find the same pleasure in having one as he did. It was obvious to him that none of them had ever even heard of a wheel. As a matter of fact, his tales of his dreams of running the National Rat Peddling Contest did nothing more than leave blank looks of confusion on all of their faces.

A mere two hours of sleep left Reggie feeling refreshed and ready to tackle the daylight hours. Normally the light would cause him to drift off to sleep, but today, he was on a mission. He would not allow daylight to be a factor in his quest. He was determined now, more than ever, to find his Billy.

The good-byes were short, but not left without a wish of good luck from both parties. Each of them, Reggie and Arnold, would take something away from their brief encounter. It was two different worlds passing in the night, but a part of those different worlds would remain with each of them forever.

Scurrying across the grass and dirt, Reggie did not have time to allow his sadness of missing Billy to fill his heart. Burying it down deep inside, he pushed harder and harder, further and further through the path of trees on his quest. Not having any sense of real time, Reggie had no idea that only four hours had passed before the heat of the sun and the light of day gave way to his normal routine. At long last, he lay down and drifted off into a deep sleep.

When darkness finally fell amongst the trees, Reggie instantly awoke. He could hear the sounds of crickets lurking around him. Immediately he felt that he had lost valuable time due to his sleep and without haste, he scampered forward.

With one foot in front of the other, Reggie suddenly froze. He could hear them. He recognized the sounds of human laughter. His heart instantly skipped a beat.

"That's just silly, Maggie. Billy has no idea who you are!"

Billy? She just said Billy! I know I heard her say Billy!

"Yes, he does. I spoke with him two days ago, just after school."

"That's because you two were standing next to each other waiting for the bus! I bet he wouldn't remember you tomorrow if you saw him again."

Maggie let a frown appear on her face.

"Yes he would. You're just jealous!"

"No I'm not!" Sarah retorted. "I know Billy. He's in two of my classes…he just isn't into girls."

"Maybe not yet…"

The girlish giggles continued. Reggie remained on the other side of the bushes listening intently. *Oh my gosh…are they talking about MY Billy?*

He lay down and cocked his ear to one side, desperately trying to hear and understand every word they were saying. Were they two of the human creatures that Arnold spoke of—the kind that would try to put him to an early death if he appeared in front of them—or the kind like Billy and his family? He had to devise a plan. He had to find out if they were friend or foe. Crouching down into a comfortable position, he listened further.

"He is really cute though Sarah. I need to find out what he likes so I can have another conversation with him."

"Well, I hope you're into animals with fur and four legs, cause that's what he's into."

"Does he have a dog?"

"No, believe it or not, he's into rodents. He has a pet rat!"

"What?"

"Yep, he actually has a pet rat."

"Yuck!" Maggie's face was now crunched in a severe frown. "That's gross!"

Sarah instantly turned to look at her, "No it's not. Rats are actually pretty cool. When we lived in Florida my best friend Angie had two pet rats. Their names were Sonny and Cher. They were both boy rats, but she named them that anyway. They were really neat!"

"I can't believe you had a friend who had pet rats!"

"Rats actually make very good pets, Maggie."

Reggie's ears instantly rose into a stand up position. *She does know my Billy! It has to be my Billy…it just has to be!*

"Wow, look at the time, Maggie. I have to go inside now."

"Okay, same time tomorrow?"

"Same time!"

Reggie watched in silence as Maggie got up and walked away. He missed his chance this time, but tomorrow would be a different story. He was sure they had been discussing his Billy. He would seek their help to find his way back home. When Sarah disappeared into the house, Reggie slowly ventured out to survey the surroundings. In the stillness of the night he saw the concrete step they had been sitting on, attached to the front door that Sarah had just closed. Beautiful shrubbery surrounded the entire front casing of the house. It appeared safe. He could go and hide in those bushes and wait for them to return tomorrow. So, when he was sure the coast was clear, he darted out from around the side of the house. He made himself a little nest behind one of the shrubs, directly next to the house. Although he wasn't sure how he would sleep in the darkness, he promised himself he would.

The next evening, just as he had anticipated, he watched Maggie ring the doorbell, and Sarah suddenly appeared. After yelling back to her mother inside that she would be just outside the door, she gently closed it and joined Maggie on the concrete step.

This is my chance. I have to do it! Reggie's mind was full of fear, but realizing it was his only shot at finding Billy, he instantly moved one foot in front of the other. As the girls giggled about happenings at school that day, Reggie ran along side of the concrete, and stopped just in front of them, in plain view, with nothing to shield him.

"Eeeeeek!" Maggie's scream was loud. She instantly lifted her hands to her face and raised her knees up to her chin.

Sarah, in total calmness, looked down at him.

"Oh my god! It's a rat!" Maggie turned her head to the side.

Sarah said nothing. She simply stared at Reggie. The silence between them was crushing, but the gaze between their eyes was immeasurable. Reggie felt no fear staring deep into her eyes. Sitting up on his hind legs, he lifted his front legs into the air.

"Sarah…do something!"

Sarah cautiously stretched out her hand. Reggie did not hesitate to sniff it.

"Maggie, this is not a wild rat…calm down."

Barely turning her head, Maggie peered at the two of them out of the corner of her eye.

"How can you know that?"

"Because wild rats are extremely afraid of people. This one is not. If he was, he wouldn't have walked straight up to me."

Slowly, Sarah reached down and picked up Reggie. Holding him close to her body, she quietly whispered in his ear.

"What are you doing out here little guy?"

Reggie stared up at her with pleading eyes. Instantly he could feel her compassion.

I'm lost. I want to find my Billy. I think you can help me!

Maggie slowly turned her head. She was in disbelief at the way Sarah was softly stroking Reggie's fur and whispering soft words into his ears. Suddenly her fears and apprehension began to subside. She thought it was strange, but she was almost sure there was some kind of communication going on between the two of them. With a shaking hand, she slowly reached over and with only one finger, hesitantly patted him on the head. Reggie turned to face her in recognition, and managed a faint smile that let her know he was not an enemy.

"Wow, he is really calm. That's unbelievable!" With every soft stroke, Maggie's smile grew wider and wider.

"I wonder how we can help him find his home." Sarah's words were filled with concern.

"Can't you take care of him while we put up posters in the neighborhood?"

Sarah almost laughed at Maggie's words. Two minutes ago she was deathly afraid of little Reggie. Now she was willing to put up posters to help find his owners.

"I wish I could, but I know my mom. She didn't like the fact that Angie had rats as pets. I know there is no way she will let me keep this little guy."

"So what are you going to do?"

Sarah thought for a minute. "Well, I know we can't leave him outside. Anything could happen to him. I'm sure if I ask my mom he can stay with us for one night if I keep him in my room. I'll search on the computer tonight and hopefully find a place that takes lost rats."

That night, little Reggie slept in a makeshift home of cardboard next to Sarah's bed. He didn't have a wheel to run on, but he had the comfort of knowing that his struggle on the outside was over. He was sure that Sarah was going to help him find Billy. He had no idea that the leap for joy she displayed while searching the internet was due to finding a place called Critter Heaven Small Animal Rescue. He thought she had found Billy.

The next morning, Sarah got a small box ready for Reggie's transport. Reggie stood up on his hind legs with his tiny arms lifted in the air. He seemed to be smiling at her in appreciation as Sarah gently picked him up and placed him in the box. Today her mother was driving her to school so they could take Reggie to the shelter before her classes. Sarah had a strong sense of self-satisfaction in knowing that she was helping little Reggie. She couldn't help but wonder what would have happened to him had it been someone else who had discovered him wandering around.

When the box was finally opened, Reggie poked out his little head. Sarah was no where to be seen. He looked up at the stranger that gently lifted him from the box and placed him inside a cage with several other rats. He felt no fear about his new roommates as he could sense they were exactly like him. What he did feel was a huge sense of confusion. He had expected to be going home. He had expected to see Billy.

Where am I? What is this place?

Tofu was the first to speak up. *This is Critter Heaven Small Animal Rescue.*

Reggie tilted his head to one side. *What is that?*

It's a place that helps us find new homes when our prior owners get rid of us.

But Billy didn't get rid of me. It was all my fault. I got lost. I was playing a game of hide and seek and accidentally ended up outside. That's how I got lost!

So how did you end up here?

Reggie quickly got comfortable and told them his story of finding Sarah, who he thought was going to help him find his way home.

Lionel shook his head. *You are one very lucky rat. I wouldn't count on seeing Billy again, but you should be thankful you wound up here. Being outside is not a place for rats like us!*

Reggie spoke not another word. He edged his way over to the corner of the cage, curled up and sighed. He suddenly realized he was not going to see Billy again. In time and with a little luck, he would find another new owner, but it wasn't going to be Billy. Closing his eyes he thought back on his journey. Lionel was right. Just to be safe and inside a cage after all he'd been through, he was one very lucky rat.

The next day Reggie lay on the soft bedding in his temporary home. Thoughts of Sarah entered his mind and caused a smile to form on his tiny little lips. She may not have kept him and she may not have reunited him with Billy, but she did save him. Life out in the wilderness could have brought so many tragedies. He thought of Arnold and his family and wondered how they were doing. He decided then that if he couldn't find Billy, he would keep his hopes up. He would at least find another family to love him.

It only took two short weeks before Reggie's faith proved to be worth keeping. On a bright, sunny Saturday morning he found himself cradled against the neck of the young boy who would take him home. The boy's words were soothing sounds to his ears.

"It's him, Mom!"

With a gentle stroke of his fur, Reggie knew this was the day he would be leaving Critter Heaven Small Animal Rescue. He knew this was the day he was going home.

reggie the rat

THE IMPORTANCE OF ADOPTION

"Mom…mom! Look!"

Mrs. Nelson walked over to her son and looked down at the cage, staring directly at the little rat standing up on his hind legs, waving his two front legs frantically at the bars of the cage. She could almost swear he was jumping up and down. His little mouth was moving feverishly, almost as if he was trying to shout out words.

"Look at the little black spot to the left of his nose!"

Mrs. Nelson stared hard at little Reggie. There was no doubt the black spot stood out, but she was sure that many rats had markings that were similar. She glanced around at the other rats in the cages. Nodding her head, she reassured herself that they all did look very much alike, less for their coloring and a few markings here and there. There were several that looked just like their previous rat. Leaning over, she rested her hand on her son's shoulder.

"Let's look at all the rats they have before making a decision." Gently she led him away from the cage. Her thought, although she would never admit it, was for her son to find a different colored rat than the one he had before. She wanted to encourage him to form a new bond, with a new animal. She feared that if he selected one that was almost identical, he would try to rekindle his old connection. She wanted him to leave those memories behind and begin new ones.

Karen Nelson could not believe how many rats were up for adoption at the facility. She had only learned of its existence a week earlier when a co-worker told her about the ferret he and his wife had adopted. Karen was well aware that there were shelters everywhere with dogs and cats up for adoption, but she had never heard of any place that had small animals for adoption. Had she known about it, they would have adopted their first rat instead of buying it.

As they walked around the cages surveying the rats, Karen reflected back on the conversation she had had with her son earlier in the week.

"But mom! I don't want someone else's rat. I don't want to adopt a used rat; I want to buy a new one!"

"They are not "used" animals, honey. They are loving little creatures who need a second chance in life. There are many reasons why animals end up in shelters, but whatever their reason, they need someone to love and care for them. Adopted animals have a very deep devotion to their new owners."

She had chosen her words very carefully. Although she knew that she had not fully convinced him to adopt an animal, she was proud of the fact that she had at least convinced him to consider the possibility.

With every cage they stopped at, Karen could not help but notice that her son was continually glancing back over his shoulder at the very first cage they visited. Trying to turn his focus away from that cage, she pointed out the other animals that were up for adoption.

"Honey, look at these guys! Are you sure you want another rat? We could adopt a guinea pig instead."

"No, mom. I don't want a guinea pig. I want another rat."

"Okay. Well what about this one?" She pointed to a beautiful, light-cream-colored female rat.

He just shook his head. Looking up at her with pleading eyes, she could clearly read his thoughts.

"You want to go back and look at the first rat, don't you?"

A simple nod was his only answer.

"Okay, let's find a volunteer to get him out of his cage."

Before Karen could find a volunteer, her son was back at the first cage they had visited. Poking his fingers through the bars, he scratched Reggie behind his ears. Again, Reggie stood up on his hind legs.

By the time Karen and the volunteer returned to the cage, Karen could already see the gleam in her son's eyes. The volunteer unlocked the cage and opened up the door. Her son picked up Reggie and cradled him close to his neck.

"It's him, Mom! It's him."

Reggie snuggled up in total comfort against the small neck. His heart was ex-
ploding with happiness. Giving small, nibble-size kisses, he crawled along the
boy's back and came to rest on his right shoulder.

"I don't know how mom, but it IS him! IT'S REGGIE!"

Karen was shocked by Billy's words. She knew how close the two of them had
been, so if anyone could know it was Reggie, it would be Billy. Still she could
not believe the possibility.

Reggie stared into her eyes. Suddenly, he stood straight up on his back legs
and began frantically waving his front feet in the air. *It is me, Karen, it is!* That
motion, the same one Reggie did all the time at home while on Billy's shoulder,
told her that her son was right. He had found Reggie. Astonished, she turned
and faced the volunteer.

"When did this rat come to your facility?"

"About two weeks ago. A little girl and her mother brought him in. They said
they found him right outside their house."

"You're kidding. Where do they live?"

"Well, I can't furnish that information, but I can tell you it was in the Willow
Creek subdivision."

Karen turned eight shades of white. Willow Creek was *their* housing subdivision. She immediately turned and looked again at Reggie.

"This is so unbelievable!"

"I told you mom, I told you! This is REGGIE! I know it!"

On the drive home, Billy stared out the window while constantly stroking Reggie's fur. Curled up on Billy's shoulder, Reggie slept. After a long period of silence, Billy finally turned to face his mom.

"Mom?"

"Yes, Billy?"

"Thank you."

Karen smiled. "For what Billy?"

A small tear formed in the corner of his eyes.

"For what you told me about adoption and saving the lives of animals. If you hadn't convinced me how important it was, if you hadn't told me about all the wonderful animals that wind up in shelters, I would have never found Reggie."

Karen reached over and patted her son's shoulder. A huge smile swept across her lips. Billy glanced down at Reggie, still sleeping soundly on his shoulder.

"Mom?"

"What Billy?"

"If we ever do get a dog like dad has talked about, will you promise that we will adopt it and not buy it?"

"You bet we will, Billy…you bet we will!

bonnie the bunny

CHAPTER FOUR

bonnie the bunny

THE EASTER PRESENT

Bonnie sat behind a thick, tall tree watching Lonnie diligently working beneath the hood of his truck. She wanted desperately to run right up to him, to seek some kind of shelter from her unknown life, but she was scared. She had never found herself in such a predicament before, amid such wide-open space. Suddenly the front door to the house opened and a little boy appeared. Closing the door behind him, he walked straight up to the man and joined him by his side.

Bonnie's eyes stared out into the wide-open field. She watched in silence as a group of cows grazed together. One cow would slowly move while the others continued to graze, and then the others would lift their heads, and follow the path of the leader. Off in the distance was a barn. She could see the heads of a few animals poking out from the stalls, but she wasn't sure what kind of animals they were. There were too many unknowns around her for her to find the courage to move, so, she lay down and continued to watch until she slowly drifted off to sleep.

Late in the afternoon, she awoke. Peering straight ahead she noticed the man and the little boy were gone. All of the cows had ventured far across the field minus one. The lonely cow was standing right next to the wooden fence. Bonnie stared hard at her. She desperately needed someone to talk to. She had been wandering around all alone for two weeks, which was something to which she not only wasn't accustomed, but she didn't like at all. Stretching out her paws, she got up and ventured forward.

Daisy Mae instantly noticed the little ball of fur slowly hopping towards her. She let out a long, soft "mooo" as if to welcome the little creature. The sound made Bonnie feel safe. She hopped right up to the fence, but remained on the other side. Sitting down, she looked up at Daisy Mae.

Hi! My name is Bonnie!

Daisy Mae lowered her head and stuck her nose between the slats of the fence.

Hi, Bonnie. I'm Daisy Mae. Are you alone?

Bonnie appeared confused. *Yes, I'm alone. Why did you ask me that?*

Daisy Mae let out another "mooo." *Well, I've seen many of your kind running around here, but they have never been alone. They always travel in groups.*

You've seen my kind out here before? Bonnie suddenly felt a wave of encouragement.

Well, yeah…sort of your kind. They had the same body shape and fur, but their coloring did not look like yours. They were always shades of gray. Sometimes they were hard to spot because they seemed to blend into the scenery. I've actually never seen a blonde and brown bunny like you before. Even your ears are different.

Bonnie felt slightly hurt by her words. Where she came from there were hundreds of bunnies just like her. Some were black and white, some were brown with different colored spots, and some were all one color, but none of them were all gray. None of her friends ever blended into any scenery, they all stood out. She reflected back on the words she used to hear so often when people came by their cages at the pet store.

Oh look, isn't that one adorable?

Look at the coloring on that one!

All of her friends were selected because of their unique coloring. Suddenly she wondered if the ones Daisy Mae spoke of could be long lost cousins that she had never met.

Well, I've never seen a bunny like that before. All of my friends look just like me. Well, I mean, they all have different colors.

Daisy Mae looked at her inquisitively. *Where did you come from?*

I came from what is called a pet store. That was my first home. My second home was a really nice house. I had a huge cage with lots of room. I lived with a little girl named Jennifer and her parents.

Daisy Mae smiled. *Yes, the two-legged creatures of the world.* She flipped her head back over her shoulder to indicate the house off in the distance behind them. *I live with people like that too—Lonnie and his son Matthew.*

Bonnie pictured in her mind the man and the little boy she had seen earlier.

My family called me an Easter Present Bunny. I don't think it had anything to do with what I look like, rather I think it had something to do with the time of year I went home with them.

Daisy Mae shook her head. *So, if you had such a great home, what are you doing way out here?*

Bonnie twisted up her little pink nose. She didn't know how to answer that question. She reflected back on the two glorious months she had spent with her family. She had been taken out of her cage constantly and permitted to run the entire house. Her cage was cleaned twice a week and she always had fresh water, food and hay. She even remembered having her fur stroked while sitting on the couch. Life was wonderful. She had never felt so loved. Then, as quickly as those memories came, they disappeared and were replaced with memories of the day she was taken away from the house and set loose in a large, open field. She remembered watching in complete confusion as the two-legged people she loved so dearly turned around and walked away.

Well…I'm not really sure what happened. For two months everything was great, and then one day, I was put out in a big open field. My family just left me there.

Daisy Mae shook her head in disgust. She looked down at Bonnie with sad eyes.

She understood exactly what had happened. She had seen it before, although Bonnie was the first animal she met that had just been dumped and left to fend for herself.

Hop on over here inside the fence Bonnie.

Bonnie did as she was instructed. She felt totally safe with Daisy Mae.

Sit down. I can tell you exactly what happened. Someone saw you and thought you were absolutely adorable, so they took you home. In the beginning, promises were made about taking good care of you and fulfilling the responsibilities of your care. But then, as time wore on, the responsibilities got pushed to the wind, only to become a burden and a chore. Then, as the excitement slowly faded away, something else took its place.

How do you know so much, Daisy Mae?

Daisy Mae flipped her head over her shoulder again, this time indicating the barn off in the distance.

See that barn? That's where the horses are. There are eight of them total. Lonnie and Matthew love every single one of them, but they did not acquire them all in the same manner. Five of them were adopted, and two of them came from situations just like yours. They used to belong to families. They were boarded for a while and taken very good care of. Their owners used to ride them all the time. But then, the owners started coming out less and less. The excitement of having a horse wore off, and the responsibility of their care became a burden. In the end, their owners no longer wanted them.

You're kidding! Why? I don't understand.

Well, Bonnie, some people get animals on what they call impulse. It's not a good way to choose an animal, but they do it anyway. Sometimes they have these wonderful visions of having an animal, without truly understanding the long-term commitment it will take to care for them.

Bonnie shook her head. Suddenly she understood. She did have a great life with her family, but it only took two short months for her to become "unwanted." That word struck her hard. Daisy Mae could see the tears starting to form in her eyes.

Hey, hey now. It'll be okay. You can stay here and tomorrow I'll introduce you to Lonnie and Matthew. They'll take care of you. They'll help find you a new home.

But…but, if I'm unwanted, then how will anyone ever want me?

Oh Bonnie, there are a lot of great people out there, people who adopt animals. That's what Lonnie did with Spirit, Blaze, Star, Glory and Prince, the five horses. He adopted them and look at them now. They are the happiest any horse could be. Trust me, in time you'll find a new home, and you won't even remember this part of your life.

Really?

I promise you.

As night fell, Bonnie snuggled up close to Daisy Mae. She had never dreamt she would be so close to an animal so much larger than she was, but Daisy

Mae's size didn't seem to matter. It was the first sense of comfort she had had in almost two weeks.

The next morning, Lonnie was back outside, hard at work, amidst the bright, early morning sun. Bonnie lay close to Daisy Mae. Squinting through one eye, she watched the man work. She surveyed every inch of him. His exterior seemed much rougher than the man she was accustomed to living with. His clothes were wrinkled, and the shades of blue from his flannel shirt were high-lighted by the deep, blue coloring of his jeans. He seemed to have a constant smile on his face. Within minutes, the young boy stepped out from the house and again joined him by his side.

"Do you want me to go and feed the cows, dad?"

Glancing down at his son, Lonnie nodded, "Yes, Matt, but first I want you to help me with the horses."

Okay Bonnie, here's your chance. Daisy Mae softly nudged her. *Go on, hop right on over to them.*

I don't know Daisy Mae. Bonnie was hesitant. *Are you sure?*

With one long "mooo" Daisy Mae answered, *I'm sure. Lonnie and Matthew will help you.*

Bonnie took a deep breath to get her courage together. She took two hops forward, and then turned around to face Daisy Mae.

Okay Daisy Mae…here I go. Thank you!

Daisy Mae pushed her nose forward as if to encourage her to continue.

Bonnie turned back around and hopped with small, rhythmic hops. She continued to hop until she was only ten feet from the little boy. Instantly she caught Matthew's attention.

"Dad! Dad! Look! A bunny!"

Lonnie turned and looked in Bonnie's direction. Matthew slowly approached her. Leaning over, he stretched out his arm towards her.

"Hi there, little one! Come here, I won't hurt you."

Lonnie watched his son walk right up to Bonnie and pick her up.

"Dad, look how pretty she is."

Lonnie stopped what he was doing and walked over to them. He reached out and gently stroked Bonnie's fur.

Matthew looked up at his dad with pleading eyes, "Can we keep her? Can we dad?"

Lonnie shook his head, "Son, you know we can't. We don't have the room in our small house to keep a pet inside, you know that."

"But we could keep her outside. She could live out here and we could give her food and water everyday."

Lonnie again stroked Bonnie's fur.

"Matt, this is not an outdoor bunny. Look at her. Look how different she looks compared to the other rabbits we see out here. And did you see the way she let you just walk right up to her and pick her up? This is not a wild bunny. This is definitely a domesticated bunny. She has to belong to someone."

Matthew stared at Bonnie. He watched her shoulders rise up and down with every soft stroke of her fur. Her little, pink nose was positioned high in the air. He could tell she was truly enjoying the attention. But, he knew his dad was right. This bunny did not belong outdoors.

"Do you suppose she's lost?"

"I don't know, son, but don't worry. We'll help her either find her home, or at least take her to a place where she can find a new one."

Bonnie curled herself up into a ball in Matthew's arms. As he carried her into the house, she looked back over her shoulder at Daisy Mae.

Thank you, Daisy Mae. Her voice trailed off as Daisy Mae disappeared from her sight.

Late in the afternoon, Bonnie was sleeping soundly on a pillow in the corner of the dining room. She could hear Lonnie's voice as he spoke into the phone, but she didn't pay much attention to his words. She was warm, full and she was very content.

Bonnie was allowed to spend the night with Lonnie and Matthew. She did not see Daisy Mae again.

The next morning, Matthew gathered Bonnie up in a blanket and followed his dad to the truck. Bonnie knew they were going somewhere, and she knew she wouldn't return. She tried to convince herself that everything was going to be okay. A deep sadness filled her heart. She knew that she would never see her old family again, but she wasn't sure that mattered anymore. They had abandoned her, left her outside to face the unknown, all alone. She was sure, however, that some of the sadness came from having to leave Lonnie, Matthew and Daisy Mae. Lying on the pillow in the dining room the previous night, she easily envisioned life with the three of them. She was sure she would fit right in. She tried to cling to Daisy Mae's words—*they'll help you find a new home*—but in her heart she knew that even if they did, there was no guarantee it would be a forever home.

At the Critter Heaven Small Animal Rescue, Bonnie was turned over with no last words from Lonnie or Matthew. A couple of soft strokes to her fur from Matthew, and the two of them were gone. Bonnie looked deeply into the eyes of the volunteer who now cradled her in her arms.

So, what happens now? What are you going to do with me?

Crystal stared down at Bonnie. "It'll be okay, little girl. We are very successful here at finding new homes for all of you."

Bonnie was placed inside a huge cage with six other female bunnies. She felt like an outcast. The other bunnies all seemed to be paired off. In one corner, two were huddled together. In another corner, two more were snuggled up against each other and the remaining two were sleeping side by side in the center of the cage. She wondered if it was going to be possible to make friends with any of them. Although it gave her comfort to know that they all looked like her—full of different colors, floppy ears, and comfortable with the human touch, she still couldn't help but feel all alone. Slowly she inched her way over to the hay, nibbled for a few minutes, and then found a spot to call her own.

Early in the afternoon Duchess awoke.

Hey, guys! There's a newcomer! She had been sleeping since Bonnie's arrival.

Bonnie knew she was referring to her. All twelve eyes were suddenly upon her. She raised her little pink nose in the air and hoped they would accept her.

Uh…hi. My name is Bonnie.

Hi Bonnie! Moon Pie's voice carried an air of enthusiasm. Bonnie felt warmed by her tone.

One by one, they all gathered around her and introduced themselves—Duchess, Moon Pie, Maddy, Simone, Josie and Sunshine. Bonnie was stunned by their friendliness, yet confused by their state of mind. She knew they all had to be there for the same reason she was.

My, you all are so friendly, and happy. I must admit I am a little confused as to why you are all so happy. I mean, aren't you all looking for new homes?

Maddy was the first to speak. *Yes we are. We don't all come from the same background, but we are all looking for new homes!*

Yeah, Duchess jumped into the conversation. *Maddy and I were both given up by our previous owners—they brought us here. Simone was found lost wandering around a field, Sunshine over there was confiscated by a neighbor due to neglect by her prior owners, and Josie and Moon Pie both came here after being shoved from one home to another.*

How come you're here? Maddy's ears were perked up.

Bonnie was a bit surprised by their eagerness to share their stories.

Well…I guess my story is more like yours and Duchess'. I was given up by my previous owners, but they did not bring me here. They just turned me loose in a field.

Simone inched her way forward. *Me too!* She cried out. *That's why I was found wandering around in a field. I didn't get lost like everyone said I did, I was dumped in that field!*

Josie shook her head. *Moon Pie and I got pushed around from house to house, but at least the last people who didn't want us anymore brought us here. It's just so unimaginable. Why would anyone just turn one of us loose in a field?*

I agree! Simone commented. *I know there are lots of rabbits running around in the open fields, but we are not at all like them!*

Crystal interrupted their conversation. Suddenly appearing in front of their cage, she unlocked it, slid in two fresh bowls of hay, and two fresh bowls of food. She took the time to speak softly to each of them and pet them on the head before she left with the bowls to change their water.

That's the lady who put me in here with you guys, **Bonnie said.**

Duchess smiled. *That's Crystal. She's what is known around this place as the "Bunny Queen!"*

The "Bunny Queen?"

Yeah, there's a bunch of different people around here, but she is the one who always attends to us. I've heard others say that she just loves bunnies—she has four of her own.

Yeah, **Josie added.** *No one can adopt one of us unless they interview with her first. She asks people all kinds of questions. I think that's good because she makes sure that when we get a new home, we won't be returned here. She's pretty tough with her questions!*

Bonnie watched Crystal return to the cage with the water. As she left the room, the unanswered question popped back into Bonnie's head.

Hey…you never answered my question. If all of you were given up like me and are here to find a new home, why are you so happy? I mean…it's depressing, isn't it? Being here and just waiting for someone to want you?

Duchess was totally prepared to answer her question. *Well, you would think it would be depressing, but this place actually helps show you the good side of the two-legged creatures.*

What do you mean?

Well, we've all seen the bad side of people. You know, the people who get us for the wrong reasons, turn away from us as if we've become a burden, and then discard us like an old book, but in here, you see the good side of people. You wouldn't believe how many of us leave here and never return. The people who come here have hearts filled with love and compassion and they actually come here wanting to save a life. So, they come to adopt us. They want a companion, but they won't consider buying one when there are so many of us in shelters everywhere that need a home. I've heard countless conversations between the volunteers and the people who come here about wanting to give us a second chance at life!

Bonnie lay in her little claimed spot in the cage and closed her eyes. As she tried to drift off to sleep, her mind could not help but wonder about her new friends. They seemed so comfortable and content in their new surroundings. She was sure that if they could be that positive about the life ahead of them, in time, she would be able to do the same. With that as her last thought, she finally drifted off to sleep.

Considering the wisdom and wonderful attitude that she had, it wasn't surprising to Bonnie that Duchess was the first to leave their humble abode. She watched with curious eyes as a little girl named Marla made her selection. Bonnie herself hadn't been picked up, it had only been Duchess, Simone and Moon Pie, but still she felt good about the little girl's selection. Duchess was a wonderful bunny, full of love, joy, and hope for the future. Although there was a certain sadness in Bonnie's heart as she watched her leave, there was also an immense joy. Duchess had found a home. Deep down inside Bonnie knew that Duchess would not be returning. She had heard some of the questions that Crystal asked. Josie was right. She did ask some tough questions, and

Bonnie had already witnessed first hand Crystal's denial of some potential new parents.

Bonnie had never understood the terms "love at first sight," "the right one" or "that instant connection" until the day that Lindsay walked into the Critter Heaven Small Animal Rescue. She had watched Duchess, Simone, Moon Pie and Sunshine all disappear with new owners and she, herself, had been held by various people, but she did not understand the word "connection" until Lindsay cradled her in her arms. That was when she knew. She still didn't quite understand it, but she "knew."

Looking back over her shoulder as Lindsay carried her away from the cage, Bonnie flashed a look of encouragement to Maddy and Josie—the only two of her original friends who remained behind. Glancing over at the three newcomers who had joined their household in the past week, she realized that she had no concept of time. She had no idea that she had only been at the shelter for two and a half weeks. Lost *without a home* had seemed like an eternity. The warmth of Lindsay's shoulder gave her a tremendous sense of peace. She knew she was headed for a great life. She could not, however, at that point, know just how great that life was going to be.

bonnie the bunny

AN EASTER PRESENT TIMES TWO

Bonnie remained perfectly still in her box on the passenger seat of the car. With closed eyes, she listened to the soft sounds coming from the radio. She didn't know the style of music was called jazz, but she liked it. No words, just soothing tunes flowing through the air. It gave her a wonderful feeling.

When the car stopped, Lindsay picked up the box and carried Bonnie into her new home. Bonnie had no sense of fear, only the excitement of having a new home. When her box was finally opened, her little eyes peered up at Lindsay.

"Here's your new home Bonnie!" Lindsay gently picked her up and placed her into the open cage.

Bonnie sat on the floor of the cage and marveled at its size. *Wow! This isn't a house, it's a mansion!* She had never seen one so big.

Lindsay reached in and gently stroked her fur.

"Go ahead and explore. Get used to your new home."

Bonnie hopped over to one corner to inspect the big, wooden box. It was much bigger than the hide-a-home she had with her previous owners. Poking her head inside the opening, she couldn't help but smile. There was so much space in it. She darted inside, ran around in a circle, and then poked her head outside. Lindsay wasn't there anymore.

Hopping around the cage, she inspected the food bowl. She took a piece of the freshly cut carrot, nibbled on it, and then ran over to the hay bin. Sitting down, several toys were staring her in the face. She wasn't sure exactly what they were for as she'd never had a bunny toy before. Suddenly a large purple igloo on the other side of the cage caught her attention.

Wow, another place to hide! Immediately she darted over towards it.

Poking her head inside, she suddenly stopped and then quickly jerked her head away from the opening. She had to blink twice. Hesitating for a brief moment, she cautiously allowed her eyes to peer back into it. She hadn't anticipated what she saw. It took her several moments of silence before she finally spoke.

Uh…hello? Is it okay if I join you?

The two small eyes stared at her, but nothing was said. Bonnie immediately could sense the sadness. She decided to back away.

My name is Bonnie. I'll leave you alone now. If you want to talk I'll be across the cage in the wooden box okay?

With no response, Bonnie hopped back over to the other side of the cage. Curling up inside the box, she was happier than she ever thought she would be. *Gosh, not only a new home, but a new friend!*

It wasn't long before Babe inched her way out and over to the other side of the cage. She was very curious. She slowly approached the wooden box, and just as Bonnie had done earlier, kept her head outside, and peered through the opening. Bonnie immediately sensed her presence and opened her eyes.

The two stared at each other for what seemed like an eternity to Bonnie. There was something about the little bunny to which she felt very drawn. She couldn't pinpoint what it was, but there was something lingering in the air that seemed to make her special. Bonnie waited patiently. She didn't want to be the first to speak.

You said your name was Bonnie?

Bonnie immediately broke out her best bunny smile and nodded. *Yeah, I'm Bonnie. What's your name?*

I'm Babe.

Do you want to come in and join me?

Babe nodded. Slowly she inched her way into the big wooden box.

Are you going to be living here?

Yes, Bonnie answered. *I hope that's okay with you.*

Again Babe nodded. *Actually, that would be great. I could use the company. It's been lonely here without Bagels.*

Was Bagels your friend?

She was my best friend. We had a short, but great life together until she got really sick. Lindsay did everything she could for her, but we ended up losing her.

Gosh Babe, I'm so sorry.

Bonnie edged closer to Babe and listened intently as she told her tales of her life with Bagels and Lindsay. Bonnie could hear the fondness she had for Bagels in her voice, and every time she mentioned Lindsay's name, sparkles lit up her eyes. Bonnie felt closer to her with every story. Her own sadness over being abandoned now seemed so unimportant. The weight of Babe's sadness was heavier. She had lost her best friend.

Their conversation lasted just long enough to cause them to close their eyes and drift off to sleep. They were snuggled tightly together. Lindsay had checked on them several times, although they did not know it. Each time she passed the cage, she couldn't help but smile to herself. She knew she had done the right thing by adopting Bonnie.

Bonnie stirred in her sleep. Opening her eyes, she glanced over at Babe. Suddenly she felt it again—that same feeling that she had experienced earlier. She wished she could figure out what it was about Babe that made her feel the way she did. Closing her eyes, she drifted back off to sleep.

The next day Babe and Bonnie chased each other around the entire house. Lindsay laughed every time they hopped by her. It gave her such pleasure to see Babe back to her old self, no longer sitting around spending her time thinking about Bagels. It didn't take Babe and Bonnie very long to completely wear themselves out. Curled up together off in a corner of the living room, they continued their conversation from the previous day.

So tell me, Babe, how in the world were you lucky enough to find Lindsay?

Oh, I didn't find her, she found me. I originally came from a pet store. I was bought as an Easter present for a little boy, but that didn't last long. I think I may have been there for a month. Then I went to a place called Critter Heaven Small Animal Rescue. That's where I met Bagels, and that's where Lindsay found me. She adopted both of us at the same time.

Bonnie's eyes grew extremely wide. The coincidence struck her hard.

That's where Lindsay got me! She adopted me too!

The two of them closed their eyes. Both wearing big bunny smiles, they drifted off to sleep.

Again, Bonnie stirred in her sleep. This time when she opened her eyes, she sat straight up. With wide eyes, she stared at Babe. An overwhelming sensation shot through her little body. She had been so surprised when she discovered that they had come from the same shelter and that they had both been initially purchased for Easter presents, that she thought she had finally figured it out. She was positive that was the connection that drew her so close to Babe. Now an entire new revelation stood before her. After a few moments of silence, she finally spoke.

Beatrice? She nudged Babe's fur, *Beatrice?*

With her eyes still closed, Babe's ears perked straight up. She hadn't heard that name in as long as she could remember.

Beatrice? Bonnie repeated the name.

Suddenly Babe opened her eyes as wide as they could open. She turned her head and looked straight at Bonnie. Staring deep into her eyes, that same sensation that Bonnie had felt shot through every tiny vein in her body. She too thought the exact same thing. *No, it can't possibly be!*

Finally she softly spoke…*Betty?*

Bunny tears began to flow from both of their eyes. Bonnie could say nothing. All she could do was nod her head.

The bond that was sensed, but not understood, was now clearly in view for all to see.

Beatrice and Betty, the two bunnies who had spent three months in a cage together at the pet store before going their separate ways, were now Babe and Bonnie, Lindsay's adopted bunny kids.

frankie the ferret

CHAPTER FIVE

frankie the ferret

LEFT BEHIND

Frankie edged his nose out from around the corner of the closet door. His eyes peered around the empty room. It was quiet. It was too quiet. Pausing briefly to survey the emptiness of the room, he slowly crept out into the open space. Sitting in the middle of the vacant floor, staring at the four walls that surrounded him, he silently began to cry. He didn't want to venture downstairs. He knew what he would find—nothing. He didn't understand why, but deep down inside his heart he knew what had happened.

Although it seemed like hours had passed for the tiny ferret, in reality, it had only been a mere fifteen minutes. He stayed close to the edge of the wall as he made his way down the stairs. He could hear the silence breathing in his ear with every step. His eyes stayed focused on his path, but every now and then, they would slowly divert to his left. From that diversion, he could see the empty living room that lay beneath him, the one that once housed the couch, the chair, the coffee table and the lamps. As his eyes glanced upward at the ceiling, he could see the bare walls. All of the pictures were gone. Not a shred of evidence was left that his owner, Stephen, once lived there. No evidence at all, except for him.

When he finally made it to the bottom of the stairs, he rounded the corner with cautious steps. He had nothing but empty space ahead of him. There were no obstacles in his way. Off in the distant corner, he saw his four-story cage. It was the only thing in the room. He noticed the door was open. Inching his way inside, there was a full bowl of food and a full bowl of water sitting on the bottom level. His eyes opened wide. He was hungry. He had no idea he hadn't eaten in two days. He had run for safety inside the closet the minute the com-motion had started. Fearful of the strangers amongst them and the moving of all the furniture, he disappeared into the darkness of the corner of the closet. He had expected Stephen to come and check on him, but he never did. Previ-ously he had heard Stephen on the phone talking with others about a "move," but he didn't know exactly what that meant. Whatever it was, he felt sure it was something the two of them would be doing together. He had no idea that the "move" would not include him.

Entering into his cage, he went directly up to the food dish and ate. After drink-ing from his water dish, he curled up in his hammock and drifted off to sleep. When he awoke, he found the darkness of night had set in on the apartment. Normally in the evening, Stephen would have the lights on. The darkness of the closet where he had spent the past two days did not bother him. His fear of the unknown would not allow it. But now, now that his fear had disappeared, the darkness made him sad. It was a reminder that he was alone. Lying in his ham-mock, he stared out at the totally dark nothingness in front of him.

ments, but he instantly had a disliking for him. How could anyone just leave an animal behind this way? He had yet to see Frankie, but he knew he was there.

As Martha inspected every detail of the apartment, complaining with her every move, William ventured upstairs. He had seen no sign of an animal downstairs, so he felt sure it had to be on the second level. He wasn't sure what species of animal he would find, but he knew he would find something.

Entering first into the bedroom, completely ignoring his wife downstairs, he called out for any sign of life.

"Here little one…it'll be okay. Come on, I want to help you."

He got down on his hands and knees, hoping that would help coax the little critter out of hiding, although there truly weren't many places he could hide. He slowly opened the door to the closet and peered in. It was empty. No sign of any life. Standing up, he went into the second bedroom and repeated his actions.

"Here little one…it'll be okay. Come on, I want to help you."

Seeing no movement, his eyes once again drifted towards the closet. There was a slight opening in it. Getting back down on his knees, he cautiously inched his way over to it. Gently pushing the door open a little more, he spotted two beady eyes staring at him in the darkness. His heart skipped two beats, and a small tear formed in the corner of his eyes. He had yet to determine what kind of animal he was facing, but in the end it didn't matter. Moving the door completely open, he crawled inside, gently stretching out his arm.

Frankie's eyes widened at the sight of the arm reaching out towards him. Part of him was consumed by fear, but another part knew he had to allow the hand to reach him. He was all alone. He could feel how much weight he had lost. With no food in the house, he needed help from someone.

Crawling on his starving belly, Frankie made his way up to meet the hand. William felt his tears beginning to fall at the first touch of fur. He could feel the skinny little body. It wasn't until he gently pulled Frankie from the closet that he knew it was a little ferret. Holding him close to his chest, he gently stroked his fur. He knew his wife would not approve, but he no longer cared. The tiny little creature in his arms had been left alone, to starve, to fend for himself, and most likely, to die. William would not allow that to happen. That wonderful feeling he hadn't felt for so long—holding an animal in his arms—an animal that truly needed him—swept throughout every vein in his body. With an assuredness and a sense of confidence he had not even remembered he had, his braveness took over. He stood up, and snuggling Frankie close to his chin, carried him down the stairs. The first thing out of Martha's mouth did not bother him in the least.

"What the heck? What is that?"

William held his head high, with Frankie still close to his face.

"This…this Martha…is a ferret."

"A what?" She waved her arms frantically through the air, "Well, it doesn't really matter what it is. Just get rid of it! There aren't supposed to be any animals in this apartment. I just can't believe it! I can't believe Stephen had an animal in this apartment. He knew the rules. He knew it wasn't allowed!"

William stared at her with hard eyes. He had to take a long, deep breath before he could muster the courage to speak. After a brief moment of silence, he finally uttered the words.

"No, Martha. We're not going to, as you put it, "get rid of it." This animal needs our help. He needs our help and WE are going to give it to him!"

Martha appeared totally shocked. She had not heard William stand up to her in years. Her anger took over and she instantly snapped back.

"Yes, William, we are. You figure out what to do with it—but get rid of it. It's very hard to rent an apartment to people when there are animal smells lingering in the air. That's why we do not allow pets in our rentals!"

William retained his courage and held his ground.

"No, Martha, that's why YOU do not allow animals in our rentals! You have this perception that people want immaculate, spotless, and clean homes to live in. I have never felt that way! I think people want to live in a home where they can share their love, joys and compassion with the animals of the world. The fact that you deny animals is the reason why I think you have so much trouble renting out our apartments!"

William had no idea where his words were coming from. They poured out of his mouth like the sweet melodies of a keyboard from a piano player. He didn't think about them, he just allowed them to flow.

"You have no idea when Stephen actually left this apartment! This little guy has been here all alone since the time he left. There's no food, no water, so God only knows how long he has been here all by himself! You may not allow us to keep him, but I will not allow you to deny me the right to do the proper thing for him and get him the help he needs. And, that includes finding him a decent home!"

Unbeknownst to either Martha or William, little Frankie could understand every single word they were saying. Curled up in William's arms, he had to smile. He may have once been *left behind*, but he was sure that he was now in the arms of someone who would not let that happen again. For the first time in over a week, he felt safe.

Martha faced William with her mouth hanging open. She had no idea where his courage was coming from. Her eyes widened.

"William…"

"Martha, don't William me! This little guy needs help and I am going to see that he gets it. You do your surveying of what we need to do around here to get this place ready to rent again and I'm going out to get him some food to eat."

With no more words spoken, William closed the door behind him as he walked out of the rental unit.

With the radio turned off, William drove in silence to the nearest pet store. He continually glanced over at little Frankie lying on the passenger seat of the truck. He was so still, but his eyes were intently focused on William. He made not a sound, but William was sure those tiny, little eyes staring up at him were filled with gratitude.

Once inside the store, William purchased some ferret food, along with two bowls. Before exiting the store, he stopped at a water fountain and filled up one of the bowls with water. He made his way back out to the truck. With the passenger door wide open, Frankie didn't move. William set the bowls down on the floorboard of the truck, tore open the bag of food and filled the second bowl to the rim. Frankie just stared at him. He closed the door and walked back around to the driver's side. Placing the bag of food in the back seat, he shut his door and started up the engine. Frankie still had not moved.

"It's okay little guy…it's for you." He reached over and petted him on the head. Gently he picked him up and placed him on the floorboard.

Frankie stared up at him with curious eyes.

"Go ahead little fellow, eat. I know you're hungry."

As the truck backed out of the parking lot, Frankie inched his way up to the two bowls in front of him.

William did not return home that evening until very late. Martha was already asleep. Frankie was no longer with him. Frankie, with his newly purchased food and accessories, was safe and sound at the Critter Heaven Small Animal Rescue.

When Martha awoke the next morning, William had already left for work. With her morning coffee, she sat out on their deck staring at their beautiful garden.

She could not believe the night had passed without even one word spoken between the two of them. She reflected back on their conversation the previous day at the rental unit. She was still astounded that William had stood up to her, not only with his words, but with his actions.

Staring out at the stillness of the grass, Martha could feel the warmth of the morning sun beating down on her skin. She had an expressionless look on her face. Her eyes gazed around the beautiful scenery, and suddenly, for the first time in a long time, she felt a sense of loneliness. She thought about Rick and Amanda, their two children who now had lives of their own. Except for the company of her husband, their house had been empty for many years. She kept herself so busy with the rental properties that she had never allowed herself to feel alone before. On top of that, she couldn't seem to shake William's words when they had discovered Frankie—*This little guy needs us and needs our help.*

Since her children left, she had not felt needed in any way. Life had become all about business. Visions of William holding Frankie next to his chin popped into her head. She could clearly see the compassion in his eyes as he stared at the little ferret. Knowing he grew up with animals, she was sure he missed that connection.

Suddenly she felt that, even having lived a full life, she had missed out on something terribly important in life. She had raised a family and she had a wonderful husband, but she had never experienced the unconditional love, the devotion, the adoration—that special bond that a human can only have with an animal. She had never experienced sharing her life with a living soul that needed her, not just for the present moment, but for every day of their life. Now, at 62 and for the first time in her life, her heart felt empty.

It had only been a week and a half since Frankie arrived at the shelter, but he was already thriving. He was putting on weight and his fur was beginning to take on the shine that it once had. After a week of being housed in a cage by himself, he was moved to a cage with several others of his kind. His spirit was high, and he was making new friends easily. As a matter of fact, he even had a best friend, Ruger.

Four times a week the ferrets were allowed out of their cages, and placed into a huge playpen. There were toys of all kinds, ramps to run up and down and plenty of space to race around and have fun. Frankie's first day in the pen was quite confusing. He had to be given direction as to what he was supposed to do.

Come on Frankie, I'll race you!

Race me? What do you mean Ruger?

You know…race—run around to see who's the fastest. We start here by the ramp and we run close to the edge of the pen, all the way around, and see who makes it back to the ramp first!

Frankie was hesitant, but he had to admit, it did sound like fun. Placing himself in position next to the ramp, he nodded at Ruger. *Okay, say the word go!*

The two of them raced as fast as they could around the huge, circular pen. Surprisingly Frankie won. Given his condition and his background, he hadn't expected to even make it all the way around the pen.

Wow! That was so much fun! Frankie was breathing hard.

I can't believe you beat me, Frankie! No one has ever done that before! You must be one special little ferret!

Frankie smiled his biggest ferret smile ever. Extremely proud of the fact that he had won the race, his mind drifted back to his last days in the apartment alone. With no food, no water, and no hope for a bright future, he still had the determination to survive. In that precise moment, he had to admit to himself that he was, indeed, one special ferret.

It was only three days into his newly-found happiness before Frankie would understand just how special he was. Carla entered the Critter Heaven Small Animal Rescue with a solid mindset—to find, that day, a new friend for her wonderful Rambo—the ferret she had named after his rambunctious nature.

Carla had initially adopted Rambo from the same shelter in which she now stood. Just as in his case, she wanted to know which ferret had had the hardest time in his previous life. At the time she adopted Rambo, he had been the one ferret there that had been pushed from home to home before being turned over to the shelter. His rambunctious nature is what had caused so many people to turn their backs on him. She however, understood ferrets. She knew that not all ferrets were the same. Knowing he would have a hard time getting and keeping a new home, Rambo had been her choice. Now, it was Frankie's story of being abandoned and left to fend for himself that guided her decision.

In a state of happiness and confusion, Frankie, curled up in the loving arms of Carla, glanced over his shoulder to say goodbye to his ferret friends. A long, deep stare from Ruger told him that everything was going to be okay as he was carried out of the shelter to begin a new life with Carla and Rambo.

frankie the ferret

LEARNING HOW TO LIVE

Frankie was not at all shy during his first encounter with Rambo. As a matter of fact, he thought Rambo looked quite a bit like Ruger, so why would he be? He also could not hide the fact that he was ecstatic that he not only had a new home, but now he had a friend to share it with, too.

Hi, my name is Frankie!

Rambo stared at him with curious eyes. He had never had a friend come over to play before. *Hi, I'm Rambo.* Rambo glanced around the room. *Where's your owner?*

Carla is my owner. She just adopted me!

Rambo's eyes opened wide. *She adopted you? She adopted me too!* Rambo's mind quickly realized that Frankie wasn't there to play—he was there to live.

137

That means you're here permanently! Wow, this is going to be great! I won't be alone anymore while Carla is at work!

Frankie smiled. *You haven't ever had a roommate before?*

No, you'll be my first. Have you ever had a roommate before?

No, just my friends at the shelter. Before that I lived with Stephen.

What happened to Stephen?

Frankie lowered his head. He really didn't want to talk about it. He wanted to forget that part of his life. He held no grudge against Stephen and he didn't want Rambo to think bad of him.

Oh, he had to move. That's why I ended up at the shelter.

You only had one owner? Wow, I had three previously—before Carla.

Do you ever worry that one day Carla will give you up and take you back to the shelter?

Rambo laughed. *Oh no, not my Carla. She would never abandon me. She loves me and I love her.*

How can you be so sure?

When I curl up in her arms or on her lap when she's watching television, there is just this certain connection—a big sense of security. Not only does she tell me all the time how much she loves me, but I can feel it!

You curl up on her lap? Frankie couldn't believe what he was hearing. He was never able to do that with Stephen. He wasn't even allowed on the couch at all.

Sure I do, all the time. It's really fun at night when she's home from work. We play this game where I run under the couch and straight up to the heel of her foot. I nibble on it and then she tries to reach down and pick me up. But, I back away really fast and she can't catch me. Then, when her arm disappears, I go right back after her heels!

You bite her foot?

It's not really a bite—it's a nibble. When I get tired, I stop and she catches me. Well, she thinks she catches me, but it's really me letting her catch me.

Wow, that sounds like fun! But doesn't it hurt her?

It is a lot of fun and no, it doesn't hurt her. I don't bite her hard, I just nibble. Besides, she wears socks now when she's sitting on the couch because she knows what I am going to do!

That very evening, Frankie got a chance to experience first hand the game that Carla and Rambo played. He laid low under the couch staring at Carla's feet. With a little encouragement from Rambo, he darted forward and nipped at her heels.

"Okay, Rambo. Is that you or are you teaching your new little friend how to play your game?"

Frankie saw the arm coming and immediately ran back to where Rambo was waiting. The two laughed in unison as Carla's hand patted the carpet searching for him. Crouching down, he waited. As soon as her hand disappeared, it was Rambo's turn. Frankie lay low watching him as he darted forward, nibbled on the back of her heal, then turned around and ran straight back to their hiding spot. Carla's hand again reached under the couch patting the empty space.

The two kept up their game until they got tired. When Carla realized the nibbling had stopped, she got off the couch and knelt down on the floor. Peering underneath the couch, she saw four tiny, beady eyes staring at her. She was positive they were smiling.

"Come on you two," she giggled.

Frankie and Rambo edged their way out from under the couch. Carla picked them both up and held them close to her neck. Snuggling close with them, she could feel the tiny kisses upon her neck coming from both sides.

She was sure Frankie was thanking her for bringing him into their home, and in fact, he was**.**

martha's words

Our house is totally different now. It's not so quiet anymore. William is only working half the hours he used to. He's home spending more time with me and I am no longer tied up all the time trying to keep our apartments rented. Thankfully, they are all occupied and have been for almost six months now. There are no longer just people in our rentals—there are also pets. William was right. As soon as I started allowing people to have pets in the apartments, our rental problems went away.

I often think about that little ferret we found in Stephen's unit. Although I could not bring myself to have such a creature, he did, in fact, change my life. William and I are much closer now and I actually have the time to do things that I did not have before. My biggest thanks to that little guy is for my Sarah. Sarah is our three-year-old, adopted Golden Retriever. She brings me such joy in life. We go for walks together, she helps me in the yard when I am gardening and she curls up beside me on the couch at night when William and I are watching television. These days when I sit out on the deck admiring our beautiful garden, I no longer feel a sense of loneliness, for my Sarah is right beside me. I now have someone in my life who needs and depends on me, just as I need and depend on her. Most of all, she has taught me how important animals are in the lives of people.

a call to action

The perception of animals as "pets" has come a long way over the years. In fact, in many households today, animals are no longer viewed as simply "pets"— they are viewed as family members. They ride with us in our cars on errands, they share our beds, and they even receive gifts at holidays.

Considering our recent shift in perspective, there is one question that calls out to those who care enough to listen and are willing to take action. This question is as powerful as it is profound and it is something that I believe every person in America should ask themselves. It is this question that inspires books such as this one and challenges readers to pay attention to the world around them. The question? **How is it possible that we, as a nation, allow small animal breeders to sell thousands of small animals to pet stores every day, while simultaneously each day thousands of small animals are being surren-**

dered to shelters, awaiting new homes, or worse, being euthanized due to lack of space at shelters?

Baffling, isn't it? So, how can *you* help? When making the decision to bring an animal into your home, think first about saving a life—Think Adoption First! Your simple, yet empowering choice to open your heart and home to an animal in need, truly can make a difference. You can also help by making a donation to the animal charity of your choice or volunteering in your spare time to help out at a shelter.

resources

In addition to the following list of resources, please visit **www.dnjbooks.com** for additional links and helpful resources to support you in making the decision to save a life.

National Animal Organizations

American Society for the Prevention of Cruelty to Animals (ASPCA)
424 E. 92nd Street
New York, New York 10128-6804
(212) 876-7700
www.aspca.org

The ASPCA was founded in 1866 as the first humane organization in the Western Hemisphere. The Society was formed to alleviate the injustices animals faced then, and we continue to battle cruelty today. Whether it's saving a pet who has been accidentally poisoned, fighting to pass humane laws, rescuing animals from abuse or sharing resources with shelters across the country, we work toward the day in which no animal will live in pain or fear.

Best Friends Sanctuary
5001 Angel Canyon Road
Kanab, Utah 84741-5000
(435) 644-2001
www.bestfriends.org

Best Friends is working with you—and with humane groups all across the country -- to bring about a time when there are No More Homeless Pets. Best Friends reaches across the nation, helping humane groups, individual people, and entire communities to set up spay/neuter, shelter, foster, and adoption programs in their own neighborhoods, cities, and states.

The Humane Society of the United States (HSUS)
2100 L Street, NW
Washington, D.C. 20037
(202) 452-1100
www.hsus.org

The Humane Society of the United States is the nation's largest and most effective animal protection organization—backed by 10 million Americans, or one in every 30. Established in 1954, The HSUS seeks a humane and sustainable world for all animals—a world that will also benefit people. HSUS is America's mainstream force against cruelty, exploitation and neglect, as well as the most trusted voice extolling the human-animal bond.

Petfinder.com
www.petfinder.com

The temporary home of 250,000 adoptable pets from 10,000 adoption groups.

+++

Animal Organizations in Colorado

Colorado Humane Society (CHS)
2760 South Platte River Drive
Englewood, Colorado 80110
(303) 781-9344
www.coloradohumane.org

Colorado Humane is Colorado's only open admission shelter where no clock is ticking. As an open-door shelter, no animal is turned away. With no clock ticking, CHS does not euthanize for money or space considerations. It is relatively easy to accomplish one of these goals, but to stand firm for both is a Herculean task. This is what sets us apart from every other organization in Colorado.

Denver Dumb Friends League
2080 South Quebec Street
Denver, Colorado 80231
(303) 751-5772
www.ddfl.org

Founded in 1910, the Dumb Friends League is a national leader in providing humane care to lost and abandoned animals, rescuing sick, injured and abused animals, adopting pets to new homes, helping pets stay in homes, and educating pet owners and the public about the needs of companion animals.

The Dumb Friends League is the largest animal welfare organization in the Rocky Mountain region, welcoming tens of thousands animals to our two shelters. We turn no animals away.

Table Mountain Animal Center (TMAC)
4105 Youngfield Service Road
Golden, Colorado 80401
(303) 278-7575
www.tablemountainanimals.org

Table Mountain Animal Center's Mission is to provide the best CARE possible for every animal that enters our doors.

Colorado House Rabbit Society
P.O. Box 238
Broomfield, Colorado 80038
(303) 469-3240
www.coloradohrs.com

The Colorado House Rabbit Society is a non-profit organization made up entirely of volunteers with two purposes: rescue and education. They offer affectionate, litter-trained, spayed or neutered rabbits for adoption as well rabbit education programs and publications.

Cavy Care Inc. Guinea Pig Shelter and Sanctuary (CCI)
4343 S. Jasper Street
Aurora, Colorado 80015
(303) 593-2195
www.cavycareinc.org

Cavy Care Inc. is a non-profit organization dedicated to providing emergency relief, shelter, care, rehabilitation, and adoption services for abused, neglected, abandoned and unwanted guinea pigs. CCI provides community resources through cavy education, counseling, information and referral services and is funded through individual donations, adoption, bequests and corporate sponsorships.

+++

Additional Resources and Information

HomeAgain®
"Always looking out for your pet."
1-888-HOMEAGAIN (1-888-466-3242)
www.homeagain.com

You may think that your pet is protected from getting lost. But accidents happen, and some things – like hurricanes and other natural disasters – are out of your control. In fact, one in three pets will become lost during their lifetime. And according to the American Humane Association, only about 17 percent of lost dogs and two percent of lost cats ever find their way back to their original owners. Almost 4 million pets are euthanized every year because their owners can't be found in time—if a shelter cannot determine a pet's owner or medical history, the pet may be euthanized in as few as three days. To help give your pet the best chance of being identified should he ever become lost, have him implanted with the HomeAgain microchip.

Poison Control

Call (888) 426-4435

www.aspca.org

As the premier animal poison control center in North America, the APCC is your best resource for any animal poison-related emergency, 24 hours a day, 365 days a year. If you think that your pet may have ingested a potentially poisonous substance, make the call that can make all the difference.

+++

If you have a special fondness for a particular small animal or breed of small animal, there are many breed-specific rescue groups that operate through foster homes to rescue animals. You can find these groups locally through most search engines.